THE BEAVER BOOK OF
GREAT
INVENTIONS

J. D. Storer

Illustrated by

Rosalind Lobb

Beaver Books

First published in 1980 by

The Hamlyn Publishing Group Limited
London · New York · Sydney · Toronto
Astronaut House, Feltham, Middlesex, England
(Paperback Division: Hamlyn Paperbacks,
Banda House, Cambridge Grove, Hammersmith,
London W6 0LE

© Copyright Text J. D. Storer 1980
© Copyright Illustrations
The Hamlyn Publishing Group Limited 1980
ISBN 0 600 34923 3

Set, printed and bound in Great Britain by
Cox & Wyman Ltd, Reading
Set in Monotype Garamond

I would like to thank my colleagues who have helped
in the preparation of this book by checking the manuscript, particularly Mrs C. L. Thompson, Mr A. D. C.
Simpson, Dr A. G. Thomson and Mr J. L. Wood. My
thanks are also due to my wife for her work in typing
the manuscript.

What is an invention?

Many thousands of years ago, primitive man struggled to survive against the hardships of nature and attacks by wild animals. Amongst these men were inventors. They invented the first tools – simple devices to our eyes but a great step forward in the process of evolution. Once he had tools, man started on the road to life as we know it today.

Many inventions are linked to discoveries, for example the *inventor* of a flint dagger had first to *discover* flint. Fire was provided by nature in the form of lightning or a volcano; man had only to discover it. But man did invent methods of producing fire, using the spark from a flint or the friction generated by rubbing two pieces of wood together. Taking the process a stage further, two French brothers called Joseph and Étienne Montgolfier noticed that the hot air from a fire rose upwards, carrying with it small pieces of ash. Using this discovery the Montgolfier brothers in the year 1783 invented the first man-carrying balloon – filled with hot air. By a strange coincidence another man-carrying balloon was invented in the same year as the result of quite a different discovery. The very light gas we now call hydrogen had been discovered in 1766 by an English scientist, Henry Cavendish, and this led to the invention of the hydrogen balloon by Professor J. A. C. Charles, assisted by two brothers, Aîné and Cadet Robert. The rival balloons took to the air within a few days of each other, but both flights were well documented so there is no doubt that the Montgolfier brothers' balloon was first. Unfortunately, this was not always the case with rival inventions, and over the years there have been many bitter arguments to establish the right to claim an invention. Sometimes large sums of money were at

What is an invention?

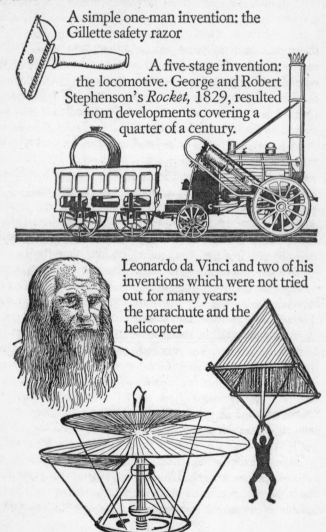

A simple one-man invention: the Gillette safety razor

A five-stage invention: the locomotive. George and Robert Stephenson's *Rocket*, 1829, resulted from developments covering a quarter of a century.

Leonardo da Vinci and two of his inventions which were not tried out for many years: the parachute and the helicopter

stake, but in other cases it was just a question of honour.

If an inventor was shrewd, he would protect himself from disputes by applying for a *patent* on his invention. A patent is a government document granting the inventor sole right to produce, sell and make money from his invention for a certain number of years. Usually this right will only apply within a certain area (often one country, like the United States), so the inventor would have to apply for patents in each country of the world in order to make sure that his rights were fully protected. However, it cost money to take out a patent, and poorer inventors often could not afford to protect themselves properly.

Some inventions were simple and uncomplicated – the work of one man perhaps. Shaving was revolutionised in 1904 by a man called King C. Gillette: he invented a safety razor with disposable blades. On the other hand some inventions took a very long time to make an impact because they were the result of a sequence of events or *stages of invention* – there were often as many as five stages. To illustrate this, consider the simple question 'Who invented the steam locomotive?' The answer is far from simple. One common reply is 'George Stephenson'; yet William Hedley built two locomotives, *Puffing Billy* and *Wylam Dilly*, which were hauling coal trains sixteen years before Stephenson's famous *Rocket*. Other people might answer 'Richard Trevithick' because he built a steam locomotive even earlier than Hedley. His first engine ran in 1804 at the Pen-y-daren ironworks in South Wales, but it was too heavy for the rails and the owners decided to carry on using horses. So where do we begin?

To invent a steam engine the inventor has to know about steam and how to use it. This is stage one of the invention and it is really more a discovery than an invention.

Then someone has to have an original idea for an engine

and perhaps produce drawings. (An alert inventor might patent his idea at this stage, to stop other people stealing it.) Many inventions stick at this second stage because of practical difficulties: for example, the steam locomotive could not be built until the working parts could be accurately produced.

The third stage involves putting ideas into practice by building a working model or a full-size prototype. This will show whether the inventor is on the right lines. (Trevithick's locomotive was definitely a step in the right direction.)

The fourth stage is to build a reasonably reliable working example which demonstrates that the invention is a success. Hedley's locomotives did their job well enough.

The fifth and final stage is to produce an improved version which is a resounding success. Stephenson certainly did this and became known as the 'father of the railways'. But as we can see, he did not *invent* the railway locomotive; it was *developed* by several people.

One of the greatest inventors of all time was Leonardo da Vinci, born in Italy in 1452. Yet most of his inventions were never tried out in his lifetime – in other words they represent stage two in our scale of inventions. His ideas included an armoured car, a flying machine, a diving suit, a mechanical digger, a parachute and a helicopter. In addition to his mechanical inventions, Leonardo made many scientific discoveries and, of course, he was a great artist. (*The Last Supper* and *The Mona Lisa* are just two of his famous paintings.) The drawings of his inventions were very clear and detailed but the writing was rather strange: Leonardo was left-handed and wrote from right to left, so to read his writing a mirror is needed! Although Leonardo intended to publish his inventions he did not do so, and most of his drawings remained undiscovered for several hundred years – by which time other inventors had had similar ideas.

In this book we will tell the story of some thirty inventions: the first twenty have already made their mark on history and are truly 'great inventions' in every sense. The final ten are more modern – inventions of the last quarter of a century. Some of these are already 'great', but the future of others is still in the balance. They may change our way of life or they may fade away – time alone will tell.

It was quite a problem selecting these thirty inventions because there are so many from which to choose. Most of those chosen affect our everyday life, and wherever possible inventions have been selected which were the work of one inventor, or a small group. Of course the story is sometimes complicated by two inventors having the same idea at the same time – parallel inventions. Several items have been omitted because they were discovered or developed, rather than invented. Chloroform and radium were discovered, while the railway locomotive, the steamboat and the aeroplane were developed. Developments involve a long process in which the various stages of invention are contributed by many different people.

Despite these guidelines it is still difficult to select just thirty inventions and it is unlikely that two people would make the same selection. It would be interesting if you were to select your 'top thirty' inventions at this stage, and later compare your selection with those chosen for this book.

1 _The Wheel_

The wheel is such a simple thing, and so common that we hardly notice it, yet the wheel was probably man's greatest invention. Would you have selected it as one of the top thirty inventions? The reason it rates as a great invention is that man had to think of the idea all by himself – nowhere in the world of nature does a wheel appear.

Nature did provide a clue, however, for a round log would roll down a hill. Primitive men discovered that these round logs could be used as rollers under heavy objects, to reduce the effort needed to push the object over the ground. But rollers had their problems. Many were needed and progress was slow because as each roller was left behind, it had to be picked up and placed ahead of the object, ready to roll underneath again. Problems arose if the ground was soft, rough or stony, because the rollers would stop rolling. Bigger rollers helped to overcome this, but they did not stay under the object for very long.

Then one day an unknown inventor had a brilliant idea: combine the advantages of the large roller and the small roller, by making a wheel and an axle. We do not know exactly how he made his wheels but he probably cut away a tree trunk to produce two wheels and an axle in one piece. This could be used to make a primitive cart by locating the axle under the base of the cart with pegs to prevent it from rolling out.

The one-piece axle-and-wheels assembly would work, but the axle rubbing on the base would result in a considerable amount of friction, which would make it hard work to move. So a development took place: the axle was fixed to the base, and each wheel had a hole cut in it to fit over the axle. Of

How the wheel was invented

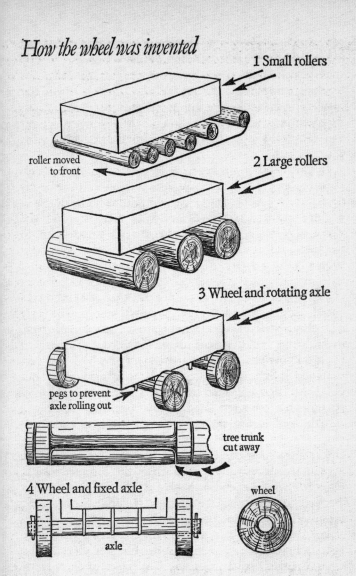

1 Small rollers

roller moved to front

2 Large rollers

3 Wheel and rotating axle

pegs to prevent axle rolling out

tree trunk cut away

4 Wheel and fixed axle

axle

wheel

course a pin was needed to stop the wheel falling off the end of the axle. This was a great improvement, but still the only way to make a large wheel was to start with a large tree trunk. Then someone invented a wheel built up from flat planks and held together with wooden or metal ties. At last we come to a wheel which we know existed, for one like this was illustrated in a picture dating from about 5000 years ago.

It was found at Ur, near the River Euphrates, in Mesopotamia, an area where the Sumerians lived. (This region is now part of modern Iraq.) The illustration showed a two-wheeled chariot-like vehicle drawn by four animals. The wheel was made from three pieces of wood strapped together, and around the rim there was probably a thin copper or leather tyre. As far as we can see, it rotated on a fixed axle.

The inventors did not stop once the wheel had been produced: they went on inventing improved wheels. The early disc wheels were heavy and cumbersome, so someone made them lighter by cutting several holes in the disc. This in turn led to another great invention – the spoked wheel. The first examples of lightweight wheels with spokes date from about 4000 years ago and came from the countries around Mesopotamia. But just a few hundred years later they were being used in countries as far apart as Egypt, China and Scandinavia. It is most unlikely that these inventors stole each other's ideas (they could not have travelled far enough). So we can assume that the spoked wheel was invented several times by quite independent inventors. The decision between 'parallel' inventions and stolen ideas is a frequent headache for historians searching for the truth.

For many centuries wooden spoked wheels remained in universal use, and only in the last two hundred years has the wheel changed very dramatically. The arrival of the railways

How the wheel developed

1 The oldest known wheel: a Sumerian cart from Ur, about 5000 years ago

2 The first simple spokes: Mesopotamia, about 4000 years ago

3 Separate spokes: Mesopotamia, about 2600 years ago

4 Lightweight wooden wheels: about 100 years ago

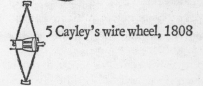

5 Cayley's wire wheel, 1808

in the early years of the nineteenth century brought a need for very much stronger wheels. Some of these followed the design of the wooden wheel, but were made from wrought iron which could be hammered into shape. The alternative was to pour molten iron into a mould and produce a cast iron wheel.

Towards the end of the century came the motor car, which was originally called a 'horseless carriage'. Its wheels were indeed copied from the horse-drawn carriages of the day, with wooden spokes and thin metal tyres. Unfortunately, these often collapsed when the car was turning a corner, with disastrous results. Some designers turned to cast iron wheels with heavy spokes, similar to railway wheels, but a much better solution had been invented way back in 1808 by the aeronautical pioneer Sir George Cayley.

Cayley built a glider which had very light-weight wheels with wire spokes. The wire wheel works in a different way from the old wooden wheel. The weight of the vehicle is carried *down* wooden spokes to the bottom of the wheel, but wire would buckle if the load were transmitted in this way, so instead the weight is carried by the spokes in tension *up to the top* of the wheel, and the rim then transmits this load down to the road. The rim would collapse if it were not for all the other spokes tying it in shape: this is called a 'tension' wheel.

Wire wheels are very light and strong but they are also rather expensive to construct. Today most of our bicycles have wire wheels but motor cars usually have wheels made out of a sheet of steel – not so very different in principle from the earliest wheels made out of a sheet of wood.

2 The Printing Press

An invention which affects almost everyone every day is the printing press, for hardly a day passes without us reading something produced by a printing machine. Yet we rarely consider how the words came to be printed in the newspaper or how the colour pictures in a lavish book were reproduced. The invention of the printing press, about 500 years ago, has been claimed as the greatest invention of all time, because it led to such a rapid spread of knowledge and information.

The first books were written out by hand which was, of course, very laborious. In Europe, this work was usually carried out by monks, who might spend many years producing a single book. The first steps towards modern printing methods took place in China about 1000 years ago. Carved wood 'blocks' were used, and you can see how these worked by using a potato! If you cut a potato in half and carve part of it away to leave a letter standing proud, then you have a 'block'. Now press the block on to an ink pad and stamp your letter on a piece of paper. If you chose a symmetrical letter such as V you were lucky, but if you chose L or F you will discover that the letter on the block must be cut to a mirror image in order to print correctly. This is the principle of wood block or wood cut printing, but instead of just one letter, a whole page of text or illustrations had to be carved on each block of wood. Hand carving just one block took a very long time but when this work was done, many books could be printed.

The next stage in the development of printing also took place in China: movable type was invented. You can see how this worked by looking at the printing sets produced for children with tiny rubber letters or 'type'. The type can be

The printing press

A simple block for letter L

half potato (or wood) cut away
to leave potato letter (reversed)

ink

print

Johann Gutenberg

Caxton's press

squeezed into a holder to make up words or short sentences, and then printed using an ink-pad. When finished with, the type can be removed and used again to make up another message. The movable type used by the early printers was made of wood or metal.

Now the stage was set for the invention of a really workable printing press, and the man usually credited with this invention is Johann Gänsefleish, or Gutenberg. Born in 1400, Gutenberg was a skilled goldsmith who lived in Mainz in Germany. He needed money to work on his ideas for a printing press and entered into partnership with a wealthy businessman called Johann Fust who lent him the money. Fust had a son-in-law called Peter Schoeffer who was by trade an engraver and a great help to Gutenberg.

One of the problems facing Gutenberg was how to produce a very large number of metal letters or 'type' for his printing press, and it is thought that Peter Schoeffer played an important part in the invention of a means for making type. A hard metal punch was produced with the letter outstanding (as in your potato block). This punch was then used to make a series of impressions in soft metal moulds, called *matrices,* and the type needed for the press could be mass-produced by pouring molten metal into these moulds: a process known as type-casting or type-founding.

This type was made up into pages with the letters facing upwards, and the page was wedged into a tray. Then ink was applied evenly over the type and a sheet of paper placed on top. The tray was slid into the press, taking care not to move the paper, and the upper part of the press, called the *platen,* was wound down on a large screw thread. In this way the paper was pressed on to the type and the page was printed. The whole process was repeated until sufficient pages had been produced, then that page of type was dismantled and the movable type re-used to *set* another page.

We know very little about Gutenberg's printing press, but it included three important features: the first was movable type; the second was an ink made with oil rather than water which would 'take' on the metal type; and, finally, we know it was an accurately-made press which squeezed together the type and paper evenly over the entire surface.

The earliest work produced by Gutenberg which survives is a fragment of a poem and part of an astronomical calendar printed in about 1448. It is rather difficult to date Gutenberg's early publications but his masterpiece was the first printed version of the Bible. This appeared in about 1455 and is often called the Gutenberg Bible. However, Gutenberg was in desperate financial trouble. His partner Fust had demanded that his loans be repaid, with interest. Gutenberg was taken to court in November 1455 and lost his case and his printing press. Fust and Schoeffer took over and carried on printing some very fine books.

The printing press had arrived. Presses were set up all over Europe, reaching England in 1476. William Caxton, an English merchant who lived at Bruges in Belgium, bought a press, and in about 1475 printed the first book in English while still living in Bruges. He returned to London and set up a printing press near Westminster Abbey during 1476.

Caxton's early books were not illustrated, but he experimented with drawings converted into woodcuts which could be printed, and these were very popular. Up to this time most books had been written in Latin, which only well-educated people could understand, but Caxton printed books with a much wider reading public in mind. Before he died in 1491, he had printed about 100 books covering a wide range of subjects from romance to history and philosophy. He even produced an illustrated encyclopaedia.

3 The Steam Engine

Some history books tell us that the steam engine was invented by James Watt after he had watched the lid of a kettle being lifted by the steam pressure which had built up inside. This is not true, for there were steam engines working over 50 years before Watt built his first engine. The inventor of these engines was an ironmonger from Devon called Thomas Newcomen. We know very little about Newcomen, even after extensive research in recent years. No portrait of him exists, and even his date of birth is not known. We do know that he was christened in Dartmouth on 24th February, 1663, and that his father was a merchant. In about 1685 he set up as an ironmonger in Dartmouth with a partner called John Calley.

Other people were experimenting with steam towards the end of the seventeenth century, and we have no idea how much Newcomen knew about their efforts. For example, a French scientist called Denis Papin built a model which demonstrated that steam could be used to move a circular piston inside a cylinder. These are the essential parts of any steam engine, but Papin did not produce a working engine. A few years later, in Britain, Captain Thomas Savery built a steam-powered pump which could lift water from a well, but it did not have a piston moving to and fro in a cylinder, nor could it be adapted to drive machines or vehicles. However, Savery's pump worked reasonably well and in 1698 he patented it. A patent was granted to an inventor to prevent other inventors from stealing the idea, but there were sometimes problems and this was one such case.

Savery's patent was very vague: it was for 'raising water by the impellent force of fire'. This was a great handicap to

The steam engine

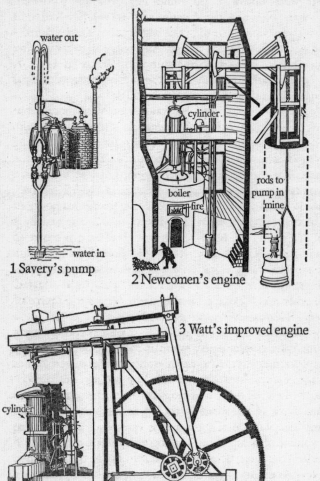

water out

cylinder.

boiler

fire

rods to
pump in
mine

1 Savery's pump   water in

2 Newcomen's engine

3 Watt's improved engine

cylinder

Newcomen who was working on an idea for an engine to pump water out of the tin mines in Devon and Cornwall. Although Newcomen's engine was completely different from Savery's pump, it did raise water and it needed a fire – so it was covered by the patent. As a result Newcomen and Calley had to go into partnership with Savery in 1705. A few years later Newcomen's experiments were successful enough for a full-scale engine to be built.

A customer could not be found near Dartmouth, but Newcomen and Calley had friends in the Midlands who needed water pumped from their coal mines – what is more they had plenty of cheap coal to burn in the boiler of the engine. The first engine was built in 1712 at a mine in Staffordshire. A drawing of it made in 1719 still survives, showing the huge engine housed in an engine house about 11 metres (36 feet) high. The layout was dominated by a 7.6m. (25 foot) oak beam which was pivoted at its centre so that it could rock like a giant see-saw. One half of this beam extended outside the building and, from the end, rods descended into the mine where the water pump was situated. The other end of the beam was connected to the source of power – Newcomen's steam engine.

Newcomen's engine made use of a simple fact concerning steam. When water boils, steam is formed, and this steam occupies a much larger space than the original water. (It has a larger *volume* than the water.) You can see this demonstrated when the lid of a boiling saucepan lifts to release the steam. Now if the steam is cooled, it condenses back into water. The volume of the water is very much smaller than the volume of steam. If this cooling operation is carried out in a sealed container, a vacuum is created inside the container.

Newcomen made use of this cooling operation, and for a container he used a large cylinder open at the top and mounted in a vertical position. Inside the cylinder was a flat

19

How the first steam engines worked

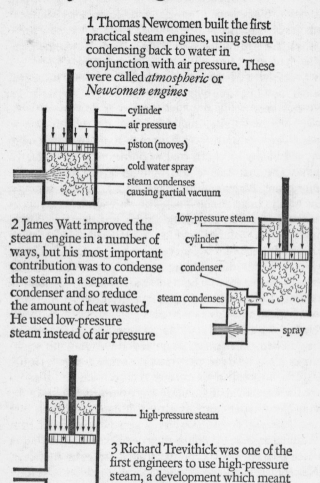

1 Thomas Newcomen built the first practical steam engines, using steam condensing back to water in conjunction with air pressure. These were called *atmospheric* or *Newcomen engines*

- cylinder
- air pressure
- piston (moves)
- cold water spray
- steam condenses causing partial vacuum

2 James Watt improved the steam engine in a number of ways, but his most important contribution was to condense the steam in a separate condenser and so reduce the amount of heat wasted. He used low-pressure steam instead of air pressure

- low-pressure steam
- cylinder
- condenser
- steam condenses
- spray

3 Richard Trevithick was one of the first engineers to use high-pressure steam, a development which meant that a condenser need not be used.

- high-pressure steam

circular disc or piston which could slide up and down. When the piston was at the top of the cylinder the volume below was filled with steam from a boiler, which was in effect a large kettle with a coal fire beneath it. When the cylinder was full of steam, the steam control valve was closed and cold water was sprayed into the cylinder. This condensed the steam and created a partial vacuum (i.e. the pressure inside was less than the atmospheric pressure outside). This sucked the piston downwards on what is called a 'working stroke'. Because the piston was connected to one end of the see-saw beam, this downward stroke lifted the pump rods at the other end of the beam, and so operated the water pump. The weight of the pump rods returned the piston to the top of the cylinder ready for the next working stroke.

Newcomen engines were slow; they did not have much power; and they used a large amount of coal. However, they were far better than anything else for pumping water out of mines, and orders flowed in.

Over the years other engineers, such as John Smeaton, improved on Newcomen's design and more efficient engines were built. Steam engines of this type were often called Newcomen engines, although Newcomen did not build them all. They were known as 'atmospheric' engines or fire engines.

Newcomen engines were mainly used for pumping water, and they proved to be a very reliable source of power. By the middle of the eighteenth century several engineers tried to adapt the engine to drive machinery which rotated, in contrast to the water pumps which just moved backwards and forwards. In 1763 John Oxley fitted a ratchet device to a Newcomen engine in such a way that the ratchet turned a shaft in order to raise coal from a mine – this was not a great success. Then in about 1780 James Pickard, a Birmingham button-maker, converted his Newcomen engine to turn a shaft by means of a simple crank. It worked, and Pickard patented his engine: an event which was a great blow to James Watt, who by this time had invented his improved steam engine. As he did not wish to pay a fee to Pickard for the right to use a crank, Watt invented a system of gears called a 'sun and planet' which not only converted the up and down motion of his engine into a rotation but also speeded up the driving shaft.

James Watt patented his great invention for an improved steam engine in 1769. The idea came to him as the result of some work he did repairing a model Newcomen engine for Glasgow University. Watt realised that Newcomen engines wasted a considerable amount of heat because their large cylinders were first heated as they filled with steam, and then cooled when the steam condensed. Watt decided to condense the steam in a separate condenser which could be connected to the main cylinder. The cylinder could then be kept hot and the condenser cool. It took Watt some time to perfect his idea and it was not until 1775 that his first engine worked to his satisfaction. Watt was a very ingenious inventor and his engines included a number of other improvements.

Just as Newcomen's engines brought steam power to the mines, so Watt's engines brought steam power to the factories. By the end of the century, Watt and his patents were restricting the development of the steam engine. Once these patents expired, a new generation of more powerful steam engines was born, using high-pressure steam. Richard Trevithick's engine, patented in 1802, led the way to steam-powered transport because it was small yet powerful.

Despite all these improvements some Newcomen engines remained in use in regions of the country where coal was cheap, even into the twentieth century: a fine tribute to the almost unknown Dartmouth ironmonger Thomas Newcomen, inventor of the steam engine.

4 The Spinning Jenny

Of all the inventions in the history of spinning and weaving, probably the most famous is the Spinning Jenny, invented in about 1764 by James Hargreaves. Before about 1760 most cloth was produced in the homes of workers or perhaps in small workshops. Often it was a true family business, with father weaving the cloth on a hand loom from yarn spun by mother on her spinning wheel. The children might help by preparing the raw wool for spinning.

You have probably seen pictures of a spinning wheel, or perhaps even a film of one being used. It looks very easy but if you have tried your hand at spinning you will know that it is more difficult than it looks. If you take some cotton wool you can find out about the three parts of the spinning operation. Holding the bulk of the cotton wool in one hand, pinch a small quantity between finger and thumb of the other hand and pull this gently away from the remainder. This is called *drawing out*. Now twist the thin fibres between your finger and thumb until they become a strong piece of yarn. This is *spinning*. When you have a length of yarn which becomes difficult to handle, it can be stored by *winding on* to a bobbin. Before the days of the spinning wheel a simple tool called a *spindle* was used. This consisted of a wooden rod with a circular disc attached near one end. The drawing out was done by the fingers, but the spinning was done by attaching the fibres to the upper end of the spindle and then spinning it like a top. The spindle also served as a bobbin when sufficient yarn was ready to be wound on.

The early spinning wheel was closely related to this device, but with the spindle mounted in a horizontal position.

It was driven by a small pulley with a loop of string round a large wheel. The spinner (or spinster) would draw out the fibres with one hand and turn the wheel with the other. This kind of spinning wheel is known by several names including great wheel or old wheel.

Then came a great invention, suggested in about 1490 by Leonardo da Vinci but re-invented in a practical form by Johann Jurgens of Brunswick some forty years later. This was a *flyer* – a horse-shoe-shaped device which rotated with the spindle. The fibres passed through the end of the spindle over hooks on the flyer and on to a bobbin. The bobbin also rotated on the spindle but at a slower speed. This cunning arrangement resulted in the fibres being spun and wound on in one continuous operation, so all the spinner had to do was the drawing out. And to make it even easier the wheel which drove the spindle and flyer by means of a double cord, was turned by a foot treadle on later spinning wheels. This left both the spinner's hands free for the drawing out.

The event which led to the 'spinning jenny' had really nothing to do with spinning – it was an improvement in weaving. In 1733, John Kay invented a loom with a 'flying shuttle'. A shuttle carries the yarn from side to side in a loom and in the early looms this was done by hand. Kay's shuttle was catapulted from side to side very rapidly and this speeded up the weaving process so dramatically that weavers were demanding much more yarn to feed their machines. Spinning wheels still had to work at the same slow pace, however, and the spinners could not produce enough yarn to keep up with the weavers' increased needs. So great was the problem that in 1761 the Society of Arts offered a prize to anyone producing a machine which could spin six threads at once. Several hopeful inventors tried but none was good enough to win the prize.

James Hargreaves was a native of Blackburn in Lancashire, where he started work as a carpenter and handloom weaver. In 1760 he made a machine for carding fibres and in about 1764 he built his first spinning machine. Some stories tell us that Hargreaves got the idea when a spinning wheel was knocked on its side by his daughter Jenny. The first part may be true but Hargreaves did not have a daughter called Jenny. The name 'jenny' probably came from engine – for most machines at this time were called 'engines' – and engine was shorted to 'gin', 'ginny' or even 'jenny'.

The spinning jenny had eight spindles side by side in an upright position, instead of horizontal as most spinning wheels (hence the story about the spinning wheel knocked on its side). Hargreaves' spindles were similar to the ones used by the old or great wheel and not the more complicated version with a flyer. These eight spindles were each driven by a loop of cord and the eight loops all passed round one large pulley wheel which was turned by hand. Now the problem was to feed the eight spindles with fibres drawn out ready for spinning. The drawing out and spinning were carried out at the same time and the secret of the successful drawing out was a thing called a clasp or clove. Eight strands of loose fibres called 'rovings' passed between the upper and lower strips of wood which made up the clasp and were then attached to the spindles. With one hand the spinner moved the clasp back from the spindles and so the fibres were drawn out. With the same hand, the spinner controlled the flow of fibres by raising or lowering the upper part of the clasp. With the other hand he turned the wheel which drove the spindles and spun the yarn – not an easy machine to work!

Hargreaves used the spinning jenny himself in secret for some time; but eventually his friend Robert Peel (grandfather of the famous Prime Minister) became suspicious when he noticed how much yarn Hargreaves was producing.

The Spinning Jenny

1 Spinning with a spindle (left)
2 Early spinning wheel (above)
3 Saxony wheel and flyer (right)

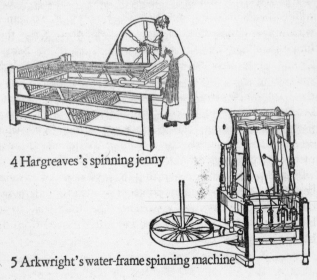

4 Hargreaves's spinning jenny

5 Arkwright's water-frame spinning machine

Hargreaves built spinning jennies for Peel's mill and for some other friends, but trouble loomed. Many workers thought that they would lose their jobs if the jenny could do the work of eight spinners and in 1768 they attacked Hargreaves' home and destroyed not only the machines, but also his furniture and windows. Hargreaves slipped away to Nottingham and built some more spinning jennies to spin cotton yarn for the stocking-knitting machines. In 1770 he at last patented his spinning jenny but he had trouble collecting the money which was due to him and, to make matters worse, other people claimed that it was their invention.

Other inventions followed in quick succession. In 1769 Richard Arkwright patented his spinning machine which could be driven by a waterwheel and was usually called a 'water-frame'. It differed from the jenny because it used rollers for the drawing out operation, and it used the spindle with a flyer. Both the jenny and the water-frame had their limitations and during the years 1772 to 1780 Samuel Crompton secretly developed a machine which used the spindles of the jenny combined with the drawing rollers of the water-frame. Because it was a hybrid the new machine became known as a 'mule'. Crompton could not afford to patent his invention and he received a mere £60 while others made fortunes using his mule. All these improvements in spinning left the weavers struggling to keep up with production of yarn and in 1785 a new era of weaving began. A patent for a loom powered by a steam engine was taken out by Edmund Cartwright. The Industrial Revolution was really under way and industries moved from the home to large factories.

5 The Threshing Machine

For many centuries grain was separated from the husks or chaff by threshing it with a stick or flail on hard ground. Several inventors tried to build a thrashing, or threshing, machine, and one of the earliest was Michael Menzies of East Lothian in Scotland who produced a machine in 1732. This was a kind of mechanical flailer. It consisted of a rotating shaft driven by a waterwheel, and attached to this shaft were a number of flails which struck the grain laid out on the floor beneath. Another inventor called William Winlaw tried an alternative method in which the machine rubbed the ears of corn out of the husks in a mill similar to a grinding mill for making flour. This rubbing action was also used by J. P. Fison, but his machine had a drum which rotated in a concave housing just a little larger than the drum. Corn was fed into the gap, and the rubbing action removed the grain. None of these early threshing machines was really successful – the ideas were there, but a practical inventor was needed to make them work.

In about 1784 Francis Kinloch, a gentleman farmer of Gilmerton, East Lothian, was travelling in Northumberland when he saw a threshing machine. He decided to make one, and, as a first stop, had a model made using a drum, rather like Fison's machine. However, his model would not work, so he called in the local millwright, Andrew Meikle.

A millwright constructed and serviced mills, but today we would describe him as a combination of mechanic and engineer. Andrew Meikle's father was also a well-known millwright who had improved the design of several agricultural machines, so Andrew had a good training. When he received the model thresher he tested it at a higher speed to see if this would make it work – it broke up!

Meikle then had an idea which combined the idea of a drum with a variation of the flail. His drum rotated at high speed in a concave housing but it did not use the rubbing action – instead he fitted fixed 'scutchers' or 'beaters' to the drum, and these beat the grains of corn out of the husks. He made a model in which the sheaves of corn were fed on to the drum by two rollers and this worked.

Meikle by this time was in his sixties, and his second son George was given the job of making a full-size machine. George lived on the other side of the River Forth in Alloa and he had a customer who owned a large farm nearby. By 1786 the machine was built and, like the model, it worked. Andrew Meikle himself then made a horse-drawn thresher for George Rennie, a neighbour in East Lothian. (Rennie's son, John, became a world-famous engineer.)

Andrew Meikle patented his threshing machine in 1788 but this patent applied only in England: he had lost his right to a patent in Scotland because he had demonstrated his invention in public before making his application. He started selling machines as a business in the following year but never made very much money out of his invention.

Meikle also invented a windmill with an unusual sail arrangement. Each sail was made up of many slats which were hinged and worked rather like a venetian blind. The mechanism which opened and closed the slats was spring-loaded, so when the wind suddenly increased in speed the extra pressure overcame the spring and the slats opened. This allowed the wind to pass through the sail and prevented the windmill from going too quickly and damaging the mill-stones.

Meikle's lack of financial reward was recognised by his friends, and in 1809 an appeal was launched: this raised £1500, and donors included well-known people like James

The threshing machine

1 Fison's thresher with rubbing action

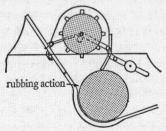

rubbing action

2 Meikle's thresher

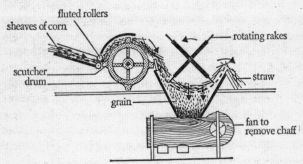

fluted rollers

sheaves of corn

scutcher drum

grain

rotating rakes

straw

fan to remove chaff

3 Thresher driven by a portable steam engine

Watt. Meikle died two years later, having lived to the ripe old age of 92.

Threshing machines grew in popularity with the farmers, but the farm workers were less enthusiastic: the old method of threshing with a flail on the barn floor gave them work during the long winter months when there was little else to do on a farm. The new machines threatened their jobs and the workers' feelings grew so strong that riots broke out in Kent during 1830. These spread to other corn-growing counties where many barns were burned down and threshing machines smashed to pieces. The riots were suppressed but they had the effect of slowing down the spread of mechanised threshing.

During the latter part of the nineteenth century most threshing was done by a machine based on Meikle's drum method, but of course a number of improvements were added. For instance a sieve was fitted to separate the grain from the chaff and a fan was installed to blow away the unwanted chaff. Steam engines were introduced to power the machines, which became large and complicated. A few farms had their own stationary engine but often a portable engine was used because this could be towed to wherever it was needed.

Then traction engines were developed which could not only drive the threshing machine but also tow it from farm to farm. These were a common sight until recent times when the combine harvester has taken over. Even so these incredible modern machines, which can reap and thresh in one operation, still use a rotating drum similar to the one invented by Andrew Meikle.

6 *Preserving Food: Cans to Freezers*

Some things are so common that when we see them we hardly give them a second thought, let alone wonder how they came to be invented. The tin can is one such object and few people have any idea when it was invented – even if they guess, they are rarely within fifty years of the date.

The story of preserving food goes back to prehistoric times when meat, fish, fruits and plants were dried in the sun. Even frozen food is not new, for the Eskimos and other northern peoples have, for centuries, preserved meat and fish by freezing it. Canned food is a more recent idea but, nevertheless, it dates back to the time of Napoleon.

In the early years of the nineteenth century, Napoleon's troops were fighting in the far-flung corners of Europe and it was quite a problem keeping them supplied with fresh food. A prize was offered to the inventor of a practical method of preserving food. This was won in 1809 by a Paris pastrycook called Nicolas Appert who succeeded in preserving certain foods in sealed glass jars.

Appert filled each jar with food, placed a cork loosely in the top, and then immersed the jars in a bath of hot water for a time, after which the cork was hammered in tightly – just like bottling fruit. Appert did not understand the theory of his process; he was a practical man and worked it out by trial and error. But it worked very well.

The next stage in the story took place in England where Peter Durand thought of using metal cans instead of glass jars. He patented this idea in 1810 but as far as we know he never went into the canning business. His cans were to be made in tin-plate, which consisted of a thin sheet of iron or steel coated on both sides by a very thin layer of tin. Iron or steel alone would of course rust very rapidly, while pure tin, which does not rust, would be very expensive. The idea of tin-plating had been tried on armour centuries before in Bohemia, but Durand's invention of the 'tin' can was an important milestone in the story of food preservation.

Durand sold his patent to a firm called Donkin, Hall and Gamble who set up a 'Preservatory' in London. By 1814 they were supplying tins of soup and meat to the Royal Navy. When the famous explorer Sir Edward Parry set out in 1824 on his third voyage to the Arctic he carried canned food – a can of veal from this voyage still survives today. Canned food was rather expensive but by the 1830s it began to appear more widely in the shops.

The early cans were hand-made in a tinsmith's shop. Sheets of tinned iron were cut to shape with 'tin snips' and bent round on a roller. The ends were then overlapped and soldered together to form an open-ended cylinder or 'body'. Discs for the ends were made with their edges turned over to fit outside the body and these were soldered in position. The top disc had a hole cut in it and through this the can was filled with food. After the cooking process the can had to be sealed by soldering a disc over the hole.

This method worked reasonably well, but an improvement was soon introduced. The top of the can was soldered in position after the can had been filled with food – so enabling larger pieces of food to be canned. A very small hole was left in the top which allowed air to escape during the cooking, and this was sealed with solder afterwards.

The demand for cans grew and grew, so a faster method of manufacture was needed. Machines were designed to replace the tinsmiths, and by the end of the nineteenth century the manufacture of cans had become entirely automatic. It has been estimated that Britain now produces over 8000 million cans every year – 150 cans per person.

Preserving food: cans to freezers

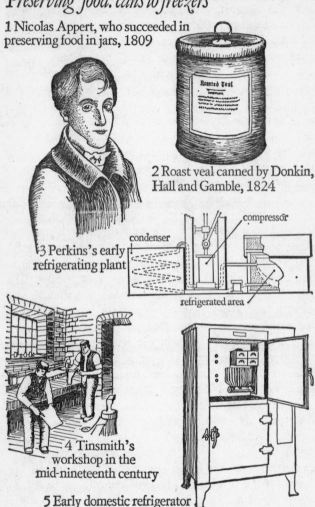

1 Nicolas Appert, who succeeded in preserving food in jars, 1809

2 Roast veal canned by Donkin, Hall and Gamble, 1824

Roasted Veal

3 Perkins's early refrigerating plant

condenser

compressor

refrigerated area

4 Tinsmith's workshop in the mid-nineteenth century

5 Early domestic refrigerator

Not all foods are suitable for canning and, as mentioned earlier, ice can be used to preserve some foods. In the days before refrigerators, ice was collected during the winter from frozen lakes and reservoirs and stored in underground chambers. These 'ice houses' would keep ice frozen for many months and help to preserve food during the summer. A few ice houses survive to this day and are usually to be found in the grounds of large houses on a north-facing slope covered with trees. Straw was packed round the ice as insulation to keep out as much heat as possible.

A machine to produce ice, instead of relying upon nature to freeze a lake, should have been of great benefit to man in his attempt to preserve food. Yet when the first refrigerator was invented it was hardly noticed. The year was 1834 and several inventors were experimenting with machines for 'producing cold'. One was Jacob Perkins, an American engineer working in Britain. Perkins produced a low temperature by evaporating a liquid. You may have felt this effect yourself if you have touched a liquid which evaporates rapidly (such as petrol or the dry-cleaning fluid trichlorethylene): as it evaporates on your finger it feels cold. Perkins used the liquid over and over again by condensing it back, from vapour to liquid, under pressure in a 'closed cycle'. Many of our modern refrigerators work in this way but Perkins did not develop his invention. He was by this time nearly seventy and had many other interests.

A few years later another type of refrigerator was invented by an American, John Gorrie. This one worked by allowing compressed air to expand, a process which can be demonstrated by the modern do-it-yourself soda syphon. When the capsule of compressed gas is released into the syphon, the capsule becomes very cold. Gorrie patented his idea but it was not an immediate success.

The man with the strongest claim to be the inventor of a

really successful refrigerator was probably James Harrison, a Scotsman who emigrated to Australia. He patented his designs in 1856 and 1857 and they followed the ideas of Perkins: how much Harrison knew of Perkins's experiments we do not know. Refrigerators to Harrison's design were made by Daniel Siebe and shown at the International Exhibition held in London during 1862; these were the first refrigerators to be sold to the public.

However, Harrison's main interest was in transporting Australian meat to Britain. Unfortunately this project was a failure and credit for the first refrigerated ship goes to a French inventor called Charles Tellier. In 1877 a vessel incorporating Tellier's refrigeration system transported meat from Argentina: it survived the journey – but only just.

The first domestic refrigerators were manufactured in Chicago during 1913, but in Britain they did not go on sale until 1924 and it was only after the Second World War that they became widely used. The latest aid to food preservation is the deep-freeze which dates from the years just after the First World War. An American called Clarence Birdseye was travelling in Labrador, where the temperature can be very low in winter, and he noticed that the secret of preserving meat and vegetables lay in the *speed* of freezing rather than just freezing to very low temperatures. He invented a machine in which cartons of food were pressed between very cold refrigerated plates. He patented his invention in 1929 and the first frozen foods went on sale the following year at Springfield, Massachusetts.

Birdseye went on improving his freezers and by the time he died in 1956 he had been awarded some 300 patents. New methods of ultra-rapid freezing have been developed in recent years and the home-freezer is now a common sight in our kitchens.

7 Photography

It may sound rather strange, but the camera is much older than photography – older by many hundreds of years. We have no idea who invented the 'camera obscura' (as it was called in the early days) although it was mentioned by the great Leonardo da Vinci in about 1500. The first camera obscuras consisted simply of a darkened room with a small hole in the middle of one wall. Images of objects outside the room could be seen projected on to the wall opposite the hole, by people inside the room. These images were very clear but appeared upside down. In about 1600 an Italian scientist called Giovanni Battista della Porta demonstrated that a lens gave a better image than the plain hole. During the seventeenth century a small portable camera obscura was developed, and this became a useful aid to artists. It retained a lens in the middle of one side, but the image was formed on a ground glass screen so that it could be seen, and traced, from the outside. A further improvement was to install a mirror or a prism which bent the rays of light in such a way that the image appeared on the top of the box – where there was a ground glass screen. Now the image was the right way up for someone standing behind the camera and it could easily be copied.

The basic camera obscura, without a mirror, had all the essentials needed to take a photograph except the chemistry. The invention of photography was therefore a problem for the chemists who had to discover the right combination of chemicals to print or *fix* the image on a suitable flat surface. For some time it had been known that certain chemicals, such as silver 'salts', turned black when they were exposed to light. A screen coated with one of these light-sensitive chemicals could be inserted instead of the ground glass screen and an image would appear. Now came a major setback: the chemicals continued to turn black until the picture disappeared. There was a further problem. Because the chemicals were sensitive to light, the lighter parts of the image turned dark and the darker parts stayed light, consequently the picture produced was a *negative*.

In 1816 a French amateur scientist called Joseph Nicéphore Niépce reproduced an image using silver chloride: unfortunately, he was unable to fix it and it disappeared. It took Niépce ten years to overcome this problem, and in 1826 he produced the world's first photograph. It was a view of the roofs from his workshop window, but it was very indistinct and it required an exposure of eight hours. Niépce's camera did not have a film: instead it had a flat sheet of pewter coated with bitumen. After treating this with various chemicals Niépce managed to produce a permanent, positive image. The camera itself was very simple. It consisted of an open-topped wooden box with a lens fitted in the middle of the base. A slightly smaller box, without top or bottom, slid down into the first box. A removable top was added to this box, consisting of a sheet of ground glass. This was the camera, but as described it would take a picture of the floor, so imagine it turned round, with the lens pointing at the object to be photographed; the image would appear on the ground glass screen. This image could be made sharper by moving the smaller box in or out of the lens box. Having focussed the image, the glass was removed and the photographic plate inserted instead – then came the eight hour wait!

The limited success of Niépce was a beginning, but two more stages were to come before the invention was complete. The second stage also took place in France, and involved a scenic painter called Louis Jacques Mandé

Daguerre. With a friend, Daguerre invented an entertainment called a Diorama. Very large scenes were painted on semi-transparent linen, and changing coloured lights produced intriguing effects – accompanied by music. Diorama theatres were popular in the 1820s and several European cities had one. To produce the large scenes Daguerre used a camera obscura and this led him to investigate the possibilities of fixing an image with chemicals. He was unsuccessful: then in 1826 he learned of Niépce's work and by 1829 they had formed a partnership. Niépce died in 1833 and his son Isidore continued the partnership, but Daguerre, by this time, was leading the way.

In 1835 Daguerre produced an image on a highly polished metal plate, but this important step forward was discovered by a stroke of luck. He put away in a cupboard a plate which had been exposed without success, ready to be repolished and used again. A few days later when he went to the cupboard, Daguerre was amazed to find a distinct picture on the old plate. Now he had to retrace his steps in order to find what combination of chemicals had produced this result. This proved to be rather difficult until at last he found the secret: mercury from a broken thermometer in the cupboard was giving off mercury vapour and this was the key to the new process. The great advantage over Niépce's method was that it needed an exposure time of only twenty minutes instead of eight hours.

However, Daguerre still had to discover a way of fixing his picture. This took two years and in 1837 he produced his first experimental Daguerreotype. The image was really a negative, but because it was produced on a mirror surface this could be angled to produce a positive picture.

By January 1839 Daguerre was satisfied with his improvements and news of the invention was released. The French Government took over the patent rights and, in exchange, the two partners each received a pension, Daguerre's being rather larger than his partner's. In August 1839 details of the Daguerreotype process were announced to the world for all to use: except prospective photographers in England where Daguerre had patented his process and a licence was necessary.

It has been claimed that no other nineteenth-century invention so captured the imagination of the public. Certainly daguerreotypists were besieged with orders, and one French painter is reported to have said 'From today, painting is dead!' Yet, there were still problems: no copies could be made, the metal plate was rather cumbersome and the surface was easily damaged.

At the same time, yet another inventor was working on the problems of photography at his home, Lacock Abbey in Wiltshire. He was William Henry Fox Talbot and, like the others, he started by using a camera obscura to assist with his sketching. In 1834 Talbot started his experiments by attempting to make paper sensitive to light by coating it with a variety of chemicals including common salt. Instead of exposing the 'sensitised' paper in a camera, he placed it in the sun with a leaf, a piece of lace or some other flat object resting on top, and held in position by a sheet of glass. The areas shaded from the sun remained light while the exposed areas turned dark – a negative was produced. Talbot was able to fix these 'photogenic drawings', as he called them, with a strong mixture of salt and water.

The next stage came in February 1835 when Talbot wrote in his notebook, '... if the paper is transparent, the first drawing may serve as an object, to produce a second drawing, in which the lights and shadows would be reversed' – in other words, a positive print could be made. Each paper negative was treated with wax to make it transparent. The negative was then placed on top of a new sheet of sensitised

Photography

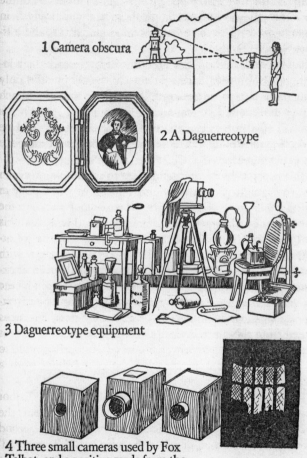

1 Camera obscura

2 A Daguerreotype

3 Daguerreotype equipment

4 Three small cameras used by Fox Talbot, and a positive made from the first negative

paper and exposed to sunlight with the result that the lower sheet became a positive print.

Talbot still had to try out his method in a camera, and during the summer of 1835 he made several small wooden cameras which his wife christened 'mousetraps'. One of his earliest negatives, taken in August 1835 using one of these cameras, survives at the Science Museum, London. Talbot continued to improve his negatives and prints but did not patent the process; consequently he was very worried when the Daguerreotype was announced in January 1839. There was great rivalry between the two inventors and their supporters, for each method had advantages and disadvantages. Talbot patented his new *Calotype* (or Talbotype) in 1841 and this process cut the exposure time to take a photograph down to a minute or two – a great advantage when photographing people. Talbot went on to write and publish the first book to be illustrated with photographs: this was called *The Pencil of Nature* and it appeared in six parts between 1844 and 1846.

Which of these three inventors was the real inventor – Niépce with his primitive picture; Daguerre who produced good pictures with a process which was soon abandoned; or Talbot whose calotype process introduced the negative-positive principle on which modern photography is based?

8   Pneumatic Tyres

The wheel became lighter and more elegant during the years betweeen its invention and the nineteenth century, but it still gave passengers a bumpy ride because the rim was made of wood or iron. We now have rubber tyres inflated with air (pneumatic tyres) fitted to almost all our road vehicles, and these allow us to travel in comfort. However, pneumatic tyres could not be invented until some discoveries about rubber had been made.

Natural rubber is a white, milky substance which can be drained from the bark of certain trees. The liquid can be converted into solid rubber by a process of heating and smoking. The modern rubber industry began in Britain and the United States during the early nineteenth century. In Britain Charles Macintosh of Glasgow patented a process for coating a fabric with rubber and in 1824 made the first rubber raincoats or *macintoshes* – the 'mac' had been invented.

Rubber was useful in keeping out the rain but it was not yet a very practical substance because it became hard in cold weather and sticky in hot. An American, Charles Goodyear, was tackling this problem and made an important discovery by accident. He overheated a mixture of rubber, sulphur and white lead: it charred but did not turn sticky and melt. This led Goodyear to further experiments and by 1841 he was able to make sheets of *vulcanised* rubber which remained elastic at all temperatures.

Robert William Thomson, one of the most versatile inventors of the Victorian era, was born in 1822 at Stonehaven in Scotland. In 1845 he patented his idea for a tyre for which he proposed '. . . inflating it with air, whereby the wheels will in every part of their revolution present a cushion of air to the ground or rail or track on which they run.' The air tube consisted of several layers of canvas impregnated with rubber and vulcanised. This was covered with leather to protect the tube from damage and wear, and the whole tyre was bolted on to the rim of the wheel. Thomson also proposed a tyre with nine tubes within one leather cover, each inflated separately – the outer ones being softer than the inner ones to give a softer ride. This would have had another benefit, because a puncture would deflate only one tube and not cause a flat tyre (an idea which was re-invented many years later).

Thomson sold his patent to a firm of coachbuilders, having convinced them that a vehicle fitted with his tyres would be more comfortable, quieter and require less effort by the horses. Several carriages were fitted with Thomson's 'aerial wheels', including the popular town-carriage called a brougham (after Lord Brougham). These aroused some interest when they were tested in Hyde Park, London, and one covered about 1900 kilometres (1200 miles) without trouble. However, the interest dropped and, as there were still many practical problems in the manufacturing process, the pneumatic tyre was forgotten for nearly half a century.

The pneumatic tyre was re-invented by a Scottish vet, John Boyd Dunlop, who lived in Belfast and, as far as we know, knew nothing of Thomson's invention. His interest started when his nine-year-old son complained that the bumpy roads made riding a tricycle very uncomfortable. Eventually Dunlop built a full-size bicycle fitted with pneumatic tyres, and one wheel from this machine is preserved in the Royal Scottish Museum, Edinburgh. In 1910, Dunlop wrote to the Museum,

'Prior to making the tyres for the bicycle I had carried

Pneumatic tyres

1 R. W. Thomson's pneumatic tyres

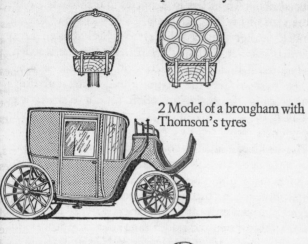

2 Model of a brougham with Thomson's tyres

3 J. B. Dunlop's cycle with pneumatic tyres, 1888

out three experiments with a view to test the reliability and durability of the pneumatic tyre. In December 1887 I made and fitted a pneumatic tyre to a disc of wood about 16 inches in diameter and threw it along the yard of my business premises. It was found to run much farther than a solid tyred wheel thrown in a similar manner. Early in 1888 I made two flat wooden rims, fitted them with pneumatic tyres and secured them to the rims of the driving wheels of my son's little tricycle. In the spring of 1888 I built two driving wheels for a "Quadrant" tricycle and fitted them with pneumatic tyres. These were completed in July 1888. The air tubes and outer covers of these tyres were made of very fine thin sheet rubber. The air tubes, though "hand made", held air well. The rubber in these tyres was subsequently used up in the manufacture of bicycle tyres. It was only after the tricycle tyres had been thoroughly tested and ridden time after time over sharp newly laid macadam that it was decided to have pneumatic tyres put to the test on a bicycle. All these experimental tyres had only one layer of cloth at the tread.'

Dunlop patented his tyre in 1888, but only after overcoming some difficulties due to Thomson's earlier patent. A number of bicycles with pneumatic tyres were built and in 1889 one won a race in Belfast. The sons of a businessman called William Harvey Du Cros were in this race and as a result Du Cros persuaded Dunlop to go into partnership. They set up a company which later became the huge Dunlop Rubber Company. This time the invention of the pneumatic tyre went from success to success.

9 The Sewing Machine

One of the greatest inventions of all time was the simple needle, yet we have no idea who invented it, nor do we know when the first one was used. Needles made from reindeer bone and the tusks of mammoths and walruses have been found in caves dating from about 40,000 years ago, so the invention must have taken place even earlier. Sewing with an ordinary needle and thread is such a simple operation that it might seem easy to invent a machine to sew. Yet the skill of two human hands proved impossible to imitate, as many early inventors found to their cost. Only when they stopped trying to imitate hand sewing did they make real progress.

The first thing they had to change was the needle: instead of a needle with a point at one end and an eye at the other, they had to use a needle with the eye near the point. Then they had to develop new stitches, and the two most promising ones were *chain-stitch* and *lock-stitch*. Chain-stitch used a single thread which made a series of loops on one side of the fabric. This was a simple stitch but it could easily be undone if pulled from the end. Lock-stitch gave a safer joint but was more complicated as it required two threads – one above the fabric in the needle and one below in a *shuttle*.

The first sewing machine was patented by Thomas Saint, a London cabinet maker, in 1790, but we do not know if he ever made one of his machines. Saint's design remained unnoticed for almost a century when a man called Newton Wilson found his drawings and made a model. In order to make it work Wilson had to make several modifications, which points towards the fact that Saint's machine was never more than an idea. His machine was designed to produce chain-stitch but he did not have a needle with an eye at the point. Instead the thread was carried through the fabric by a forked needle which passed through a hole in the fabric made by a separate pointed 'awl' – a clumsy arrangement. In 1810, a German inventor, B. Krems, made the first chain-stitch machine with an eye-pointed needle but his machine was not a success.

The first sewing machine to work reasonably well was patented in 1830 by a French tailor called Barthelemy Thimonnier. His rather clumsy chain-stitch machines were used in a factory making army uniforms, but were destroyed by a mob of angry tailors who thought they would be put out of work by the new invention. Poor Thimonnier only narrowly escaped with his life. He struggled on, improving his machine over the years, but he never managed to sell it in any numbers, and he died in poverty in 1857.

The next stage took place in America. In about 1833 Walter Hunt of New York invented the first lock-stitch machine. In his machine the cloth was held vertically whereas in most machines it was held horizontally. From one side a needle carried the first thread through the cloth and formed a loop on the other side. Then a shuttle passed through this loop carrying a second thread and the lock-stitch was formed. Hunt had trouble with his machine and abandoned the idea without bothering to patent it.

In 1846 a very similar machine was invented by Elias Howe, a mechanic from Massachusetts, who was able to patent his design because of Hunt's omission. As far as is known, Howe knew nothing about Hunt's machine while he was inventing his own. More to the point, however, Howe's lock-stitch machine with its eye-pointed curved needle worked very well and so it is usually acknowledged as the first successful sewing machine.

Unfortunately, Howe did not have instant success when he tried to sell his machine. He sold his British patent rights

The sewing machine

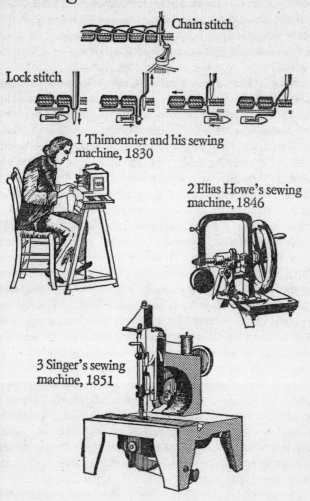

Chain stitch

Lock stitch

1 Thimonnier and his sewing machine, 1830

2 Elias Howe's sewing machine, 1846

3 Singer's sewing machine, 1851

to William Thomas who patented it in his own name, and by 1849 several American inventors had produced their version of the sewing machine. Howe was not doing very well and was desperately short of money. Nevertheless, he defended his patent rights in court and after a long legal battle won his case and received a royalty payment from all manufacturers of lock-stitch machines with eye-pointed needles.

Howe may have invented the first successful sewing machine, but the man who invented the first really popular machine was Isaac Merritt Singer of Pittstown, New York. Singer based his machine on Howe's but with several very important improvements, the most obvious being the needle which moved up and down instead of from side to side. This layout made it much easier to feed the cloth into the machine. Singer patented his improved machine in 1851 but Howe still owned the original patent, so Howe, Singer and two other companies combined all their patents and for many years this group controlled the rapidly growing sewing machine industry.

By the 1860s the sewing machine was seen not only in factories, but also in homes. It revolutionised life in the second half of the nineteenth century. In the clothing factories it reduced the time needed to make a garment to about one-tenth, so ready-made clothing dropped in price. It became possible to make extremely complicated and elaborate clothes which gave fashion designers an exciting new freedom. In the home, the sewing machine made routine mending less of a chore, and home dressmaking became popular. Even the engineering industry was affected, because sewing machines had to be manufactured in large numbers, yet the parts had to be made with great accuracy. Several machine tools were specially designed to make possible the mass production of sewing machines. These early machines were so well made that many survive today!

10 *Steel*

Steel was discovered about 4000 years ago, but remained a rare metal until an invention in 1856 made it the most widely used metal in the world. Steel is made by heating iron in a special way: iron contains tiny pieces of carbon (like currants in a cake), and to make steel some of these have to be dissolved in the iron, while the rest are removed. The early smiths discovered how to do this by a trial and error process of heating and hammering: it was more an art than a science, and a carefully guarded secret! The makers of swords and armour were the supreme masters of the art of steel-making, and world-wide reputations were built up by the smiths of Damascus and Toledo.

An important discovery was made in the 1740s by a Yorkshire clockmaker called Benjamin Huntsman who needed better quality steel for his clock springs. It was very difficult to produce consistently high-grade steel using the old heat and hammer method – it was like baking with uncertain ingredients, in an oven of uncertain temperature for a guessed period of time. Huntsman invented a process in which the ingredients were placed in a crucible and heated in a furnace for five hours. The iron melted and a secret *flux* was added. At the end of the heating time the molten steel could be poured out of the crucible and this *cast steel* was consistently pure and hard.

Huntsman's steel, being very hard, was difficult to shape and local manufacturers of cutlery tended to ignore it. However, the French cutlers bought it and produced superior cutlery which they were able to sell in England. The Sheffield cutlers became alarmed at this and were forced to turn to Huntsman for supplies of his 'crucible' steel. Huntsman expanded his business but kept the process a closely guarded secret – he would not allow strangers into his works, and all casting operations were carried out at night. However, the secret leaked out eventually, and for a hundred years it was the main source of steel, but it had its limitations. It was too hard for many jobs, and it could only be produced in small quantities – about 50lb (23kg) in each crucible.

Probably the greatest step forward in steel-making came in 1856 when Henry Bessemer announced his new invention, which could change iron into steel quickly and cheaply. Bessemer was by this time in his forties and he had been responsible for many successful inventions. He started his experiments on iron with the aim of producing a soft, workable iron, but discovered that his new process could easily be adapted to convert iron into steel. Bessemer built his first *converter* at his London workshop in 1855. It consisted of an upright cylinder into which air could be blown through the base. Molten iron was poured in and the blast of air turned on, so that the unwanted carbon in the iron burned away in the air. However, the burning carbon raised the temperature so much that a small quantity of carbon dissolved in the iron, thereby producing steel.

The great news was released in August 1856 and iron manufacturers flocked to Bessemer and paid for a licence to use a converter, but the invention turned out to be a dismal failure. Bessemer was called a cheat and a fraud. He returned all the licence money and set about finding out what had gone wrong. Two years later he had solved the problem. The iron manufacturers had used iron containing large quantities of phosphorus whereas, purely by chance, Bessemer had used iron containing very little phosphorus. The converter could not cope with the phosphorus, which was a great handicap as much of the iron ore mined in Britain contained this impurity.

Steel

Bessemer's fixed converter

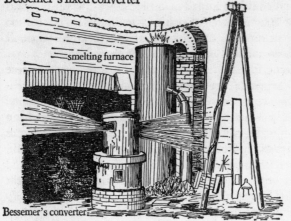

smelting furnace

Bessemer's converter

A Bessemer converter in action

Before the operation begins

The molten iron is poured in
(sectional view)

The air is blasted through
(sectional view)

Steel is poured out
(sectional view)

By 1860 Bessemer had designed an improved converter and this design remained in use, with minor improvements, until the 1970s. It looked rather like an outsize concrete mixer and could be tipped in the same way. With the converter in a horizontal position, molten iron was poured in: then it was tilted so that the open end pointed upwards. A strong blast of air was blown through the molten metal from the bottom of the converter and this produced a great shower of sparks from the mouth, rivalling any firework display. This was followed by brown smoke, a dull red flame and finally a huge white flame combined with a roaring sound – just twenty minutes from beginning to end and the converter was full of steel. It could then be tilted again and the molten steel poured into a ladle ready for casting.

Bessemer's invention made him a millionaire, but there was a less happy story in the United States. William Kelly began experiments at his ironworks in Kentucky many years before Bessemer's first experiment. He too discovered, accidentally, that steel could be made by blowing air through molten iron. From 1851 Kelly worked secretly in a forest, where he built a series of converters, and gradually improved his process until he was satisfied that he had got it right. He then applied for a patent, but the year was 1856 and Bessemer had already been granted a patent covering both Britain and America. Kelly was able to prove that he had produced a converter before Bessemer, but it was too late and poor Kelly went bankrupt. The two inventors worked quite independently of each other but came to the same solution at the same time: an example of a parallel invention – something which happened surprisingly often.

11 *The Typewriter*

No inventor, no matter how good his idea may be, can succeed unless there are people ready to buy his invention. He may suffer for being ahead of his time, as did Thomson with his pneumatic tyre or Thimonnier with his sewing machine. The same thing happened with the typewriter – it was invented several times before anyone made any money out of the idea. The first patent was granted as far back as 1714 by Queen Anne, a few months before she died, and well before the start of the Industrial Revolution. The inventor was a waterworks engineer called Henry Mill and a description of his machine from the time of his invention tells us '... that he has, by great study, paines and expense, lately invented and brought to perfection an artificial machine or method for the impressing or transcribing of letters, singly or progressively one after the other, as in writing ...' However, no drawing or model of Mill's machine survives, so we have no way of knowing whether the claim was true or false.

During the next hundred years a number of writing machines were invented in several European countries, but they were slow and laborious. In fact most of them were not designed as typewriters; they were to produce raised or *embossed* letters which blind people could read by touch. Of these early machines perhaps the one nearest to a typewriter was Wolfgang von Kempelen's machine produced at the beginning of the nineteenth century. This Hungarian inventor was the superintendent of a salt mine but in his spare time he was an inventor, a poet, a scientist, an artist, and he spoke nine languages. His inventions ranged from a steam turbine to a chess-playing machine which brought him fame when it beat Napoleon – who was a keen chess-player and not too happy at being beaten by a machine! Von Kempelen's typewriter was less successful than his automatic chess-player but it did print its letters with ink and so differed from the earlier embossing machines.

The next important typewriter to be invented was an American one, designed by William Austin Burt, patented in 1829 and called a *typographer*. The letters of the alphabet or *type* were fixed to part of a circle which could be rotated until the correct letter was over the printing point, then a lever was pressed and the chosen letter was printed on the paper. So to type each letter required two operations and this made typing rather too laborious for businessmen. However, a modified version, which incorporated a full circle to carry the letters, was developed and was very popular for children's typewriters. Burt's original typographer was destroyed in a fire at the United States Patents Office during 1836, but several typed letters survive. Having produced a machine to meet his own needs Burt did not seem to show much interest in selling his invention, indeed he was more involved with his other inventions. These were mainly navigation and surveying instruments and one of them, a solar compass, was standard equipment for more thas 75 years.

A steady stream of typewriters followed and although some worked reasonably well, none sold in large numbers. One of the most interesting, from a technical point of view, was the *machine kryptographique* patented in 1833 by Xavier Progin, a printer from Marseilles. This machine had each letter of the alphabet on a separate bar and lever. When one lever was pressed down, a letter was printed in the centre of the machine. Progin did not think to mark each lever with its letter, yet he claimed that it 'would write almost as fast as a pen'. Progin also constructed a typewriter for typing music but his main contribution for the future was the 'type bar' operating mechanism – still used today.

If one man had to be named as the inventor of the modern typewriter it would be an American, Christopher Latham Sholes, but this would be a little unfair on Sholes' collaborators, and on the earlier inventors: it has been claimed that Sholes was the 52nd man to invent the typewriter! In the 1860s Sholes was working in C. F. Kleinsteuber's workshop in Milwaukee, where he and Carlos Glidden built a machine for numbering the pages of a book. Glidden is usually credited with the idea of adapting their machine to type letters instead of numbers. Together they worked on the idea and produced a very simple machine which printed just one letter – a 'W'. This helped them to develop a mechanism which could be incorporated into a larger machine, and for help with the letters they turned to a printer called Samuel Soulé. After many difficulties the new machine was ready and in 1867 Sholes called his friends together and started to type 'C. LATHAM SHOLES SEPTEMBER 1867'. It was in capital letters because these were the only ones fitted into the machine.

So far, so good, but success was still a long way ahead, for the machine tended to jam very easily and there was the even greater problem of raising enough money to manufacture the machines in large numbers. One problem was solved – a name for the machine was agreed. The partners tried 'writing machine' and 'printing machine' but neither seemed suitable so Sholes thought of 'typewriter' and this was accepted.

Sholes persuaded a businessman called James Densmore to provide money and so allow the necessary improvements to continue. In order to stop his machine from jamming, Sholes had to take a momentous decision and rearrange the keyboard. Many of the early typewriter keyboards were just like piano keyboards and the letters were in alphabetical order. Sholes typewriters had several rows of buttons to

The typewriter

1 Burt's *typographer,* 1829

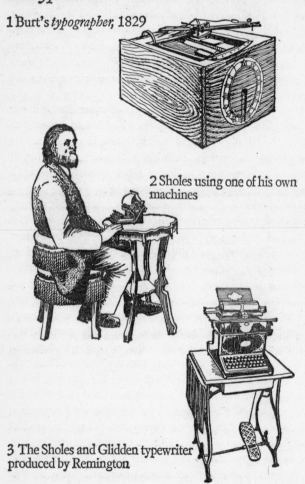

2 Sholes using one of his own machines

3 The Sholes and Glidden typewriter produced by Remington

press but he tried to keep the alphabetical order, until he decided that separating the most used letters would reduce the risk of jamming. He consulted a friend who was a schoolmaster, and they studied the most used letters and combinations of letters. After many experiments Sholes produced his new keyboard which started with the letters Q W E R T Y and despite many other suggestions over the years, this is the one in use today.

The rest of the story of the first commercial typewriter is more a question of salesmanship than invention. Densmore had great faith in the Sholes and Glidden machine but he lacked money. George Washington Newton Yost bought shares in the company and by 1873 a really practical machine was emerging with four rows of keys: one row of numbers and three of letters starting with Q W E R T Y. The business partners Densmore and Yost just could not make and sell them at a profit. But their luck changed when they met Philo Remington whose firm, the Remington Fire Arms Company, had been making guns during the American Civil War. With the war over, the factory needed work and on 1st March, 1873, a contract was signed. A few improvements were made to the Sholes and Glidden design, and it was modified to make mass-production possible. By September the manufacture of 1000 machines began, and early in 1874 the first ones were delivered. One of the first customers was the famous author Samuel L. Clemens, better known as Mark Twain, and a letter he typed in 1874 still survives. Sales, however, were not as high as Remington would have liked, despite the typewriter being featured at the large exhibition held in 1876 to commemorate the centenary of the founding of the United States. Remington decided to lend typewriters to several hundred firms and so tempt them to buy more: it worked, and at long last the typewriter became a real success.

Today when we need to send an urgent message to someone we just go to a telephone, pick up the receiver and dial a number. Within seconds we can be talking to someone who is at the other end of the country or even living on another continent. The need to relay urgent messages has been with us since the dawn of civilisation but the telephone is a mere hundred years old. The Ancient Greeks used relays of runners to carry written messages but this was rather slow and in later years various signalling methods were introduced to speed things up. A bonfire on the top of a hill could be seen from great distances and warn of an enemy attack. This simple visual signal could be extended by lighting a series of fires on suitable vantage points. More complicated messages could be sent by smoke signals, flashing lights, flags or the waving arms of a semaphore signal. Sound signals were also used, such as church bells or the beating of drums.

In the 1830s a new method of sending messages emerged – the electric telegraph. An electric current passing along a wire could be made to deflect a compass needle and this in turn could be adapted to relay a message. The whole system was simplified in 1837 when two Americans, Samuel Morse and Alfred Vail, developed the *morse code* which converted each letter of the alphabet into a series of dots and dashes. During the nineteenth century the telegraph service extended rapidly, as cables to carry the messages were laid across the world's continents and oceans. But this new service could only transmit messages in the form of a telegram and people wanted to be able to talk to each other. The problem was to convert speech into a form which could be transmitted along a wire and the man who eventually solved this problem was Alexander Graham Bell.

Alexander Bell was born in Edinburgh in 1847 and as a boy he adopted the name Graham because there were too many Alexander Bells in the family. His father, Alexander Melville Bell, was a world-famous author and teacher on the subject of correct speech. In fact, he had invented a system of symbols to teach elocution which he called *Visible Speech*, and young Graham often helped his father with demonstrations at lectures. The boy was also a talented musician and had been able to play by ear as an infant. He put his talents to good use and became a student teacher giving lessons in elocution and music.

Alexander Graham Bell studied the work of a German scientist called Hermann von Helmholtz who had carried out many experiments to reproduce human sounds by mechanical means; these included an experiment in which a tuning fork was made to vibrate by means of electricity. At this stage Bell knew very little about electricity, but his inquiring mind led him to study the subject: he installed a telegraph wire from his own room to that of a friend.

By the time he was twenty-one years old, Bell was able to take over lectures at home when his father was away on lecture tours. Everything seemed to be going well, until his two brothers died of tuberculosis and the doctors said Graham's health was in danger. So, in 1870, the family emigrated to the healthier climate of Canada.

They settled in Brantford, Ontario, and the young man's health improved rapidly. In the following year he went to Boston to lecture on his father's visible speech method at a school for the deaf. This was so successful that he set up his own school to teach deaf children how to talk, and he demonstrated his methods to other teachers. While in Boston, Bell was experimenting with a telegraph system which could carry several messages on one wire, but he lacked time and the practical skills to make the necessary parts. A friend recommended an assistant called Thomas A. Watson, and this partnership produced the telephone.

Bell and Watson's first telephone was fitted with a vibrating reed (a vibrating reed produces the note in a clarinet). By speaking into a mouthpiece the reed was set vibrating near an electromagnet and this in turn set up electrical currents which could be carried by a wire to a receiver. On 1st July, 1875, Watson sang into the telephone and Bell just recognised the tune.

So far, so good, but this telephone with its 'gallows frame' shape was still too primitive to transmit a conversation. Bell and Watson turned to their alternative design, the *liquid transmitter*. This had a thin diaphragm at the end of a mouthpiece, and from the centre of this diaphragm a platinum needle dipped into a liquid. As the diaphragm was moved up and down by the sound waves, so more or less of the needle was exposed out of the liquid. When an electric current was passed through the needle this movement caused the current to vary, so a signal could be transmitted along a wire. After several failures Bell called into the mouthpiece 'Mr Watson, come here, I want you.' Watson rushed from an adjacent room, 'Mr Bell, I heard every word you said – distinctly!'

At last Bell had achieved his aim and transmitted human speech along a wire. The date was 10th March, 1876, and in June Bell's telephone was demonstrated to enthusiastic crowds at the Philadelphia Centennial Exposition. In August, Bell arranged the first long-distance call using a telegraph company's lines. He received a call from his father 8 miles (13km) away – although the message actually travelled a distance of 68 miles (109 km) along the land lines.

The telephone

1 A morse telegraph receiver

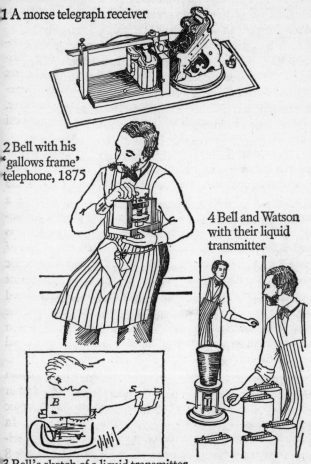

2 Bell with his 'gallows frame' telephone, 1875

4 Bell and Watson with their liquid transmitter

3 Bell's sketch of a liquid transmitter, 1876

In July 1877 Bell married Mabel Hubbard who had been one of his deaf pupils in Boston and after a short honeymoon they sailed for Britain. It was really a sales tour but Bell was looking forward to seeing the old country again: he had by this time become an American citizen. He was received by Queen Victoria and gave her a demonstration of his telephone. The Queen wrote in her journal 'A Professor Bell explained the whole process and it is most extraordinary.'

Although Bell and his assistant Watson are generally accepted as the inventors of the telephone, they were not alone. For instance, there was J. Philipp Reis of Frankfurt in Germany, who made and demonstrated an electric telephone in 1861. This has been described as a scientific toy and certainly Reis never developed it into a practical telephone. Bell patented his telephone on 7th March, 1876, just before his successful experiment and just before a rival American inventor called Elisha Gray tried to patent his version of the telephone. Gray challenged Bell's patent in court but Bell was adjudged to have the first claim. Another of Bell's rivals was Thomas Alva Edison, famous for his inventions of the phonograph and electric light bulb. Edison invented an improved transmitter for the telephone but this was quickly followed by an even better one invented by another American, Emile Berliner. The Bell Telephone Company bought Berliner's patents and employed Berliner to carry on improving his design. The patent battles continued but the telephone lines spread around the world with the United States leading the way. By 1915 the first telephone line linking New York and San Francisco was ready to be opened Mr Bell in New York called Mr Watson in San Francisco and said 'Mr Watson, come here, I want you!'

13 Record Players

Record player, Gramophone, Phonograph, Graphophone and Zonophone are just a few of the names given to machines which play back recorded words and music. The first machines were called Phonographs by their inventor Thomas Alva Edison, and their recordings were made not on discs but on cylinders; so for the sake of simplicity cylinder-players are usually called *phonographs* and disc-players are referred to as *gramophones*.

Thomas Alva Edison was one of the greatest inventors of all time and his interests ranged from motion pictures to power stations. At the age of twenty-three he had his own company with a staff of about fifty – this has been described as an 'invention-factory'. Edison was interested in sound and made several important inventions to improve the telephone, including a new carbon microphone for the mouthpiece, and a loud-speaker. Strangely enough, these inventions did not lead to the phonograph, instead the idea came from his work on an automatic recording telegraph. Edison was making a machine to record messages in morse code so that they could be transmitted at high speed. The morse message was 'recorded' on a strip of waxed paper by pressing indentations of dots and dashes. This embossed strip was then run at high speed under a spring-loaded 'follower' which moved up and down.

Edison noticed that at very high speeds the spring acted like a musical reed and gave off a note. He then turned to his earlier experience with the telephone, and designed a machine with a telephone-style mouthpiece and diaphragm. Sound waves from the human voice moved the diaphragm to and fro, and a stylus attached to the centre of the diaphragm also moved to and fro. The stylus just touched a thin sheet of tinfoil wrapped around a grooved cylinder, and any movement embossed the tinfoil. The cylinder was rotated by turning a handle which also moved it sideways on a screw thread, so that the groove formed by the stylus was in fact a spiral.

In July 1877 Edison shouted 'Halloo' into the machine and then set it to play back by placing a second stylus and diaphragm on the embossed tinfoil. He turned the handle and out came a sound – not very clear or loud, but a promising start. At this stage Edison was not sure whether there would be a demand for a talking machine but he decided that businessmen might find them useful and he asked his assistant John Kreusi to construct an improved phonograph based on the experimental model. On 6th December, 1877, this was ready and Edison made his first real recording, 'Mary had a little lamb'. On the following day he went to see the editor of the magazine *Scientific American*, taking his phonograph with him. From the strange-looking machine came Edison's voice, 'How do you do? How do you like the phonograph?'

From this simple beginning a vast industry was born, but there were many improvements to come before it was fully developed. One of the first was to replace the fragile tinfoil by wax-coated cardboard cylinders, and thus make it possible to produce recordings for sale. The inventors of the wax-coated cylinder were Chichester A. Bell and Charles Sumner Tainter who patented their idea in 1886 – incidentally Chichester Bell was a cousin of Alexander Graham Bell, inventor of the telephone. Each cylinder had to be cut individually as there was no way of manufacturing copies. Of course several recording machines, each with a diaphragm, cutting stylus and wax-coated cylinder, could be set up for a single performance by an artist. But even if five machines

Record players

1 Edison's 'talking phonograph' from *The Scientific American* of 22 December 1877

2 Edison Gem phonograph, c. 1903

3 Berliner gramophone, c. 1893

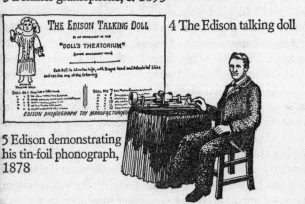

4 The Edison talking doll

THE EDISON TALKING DOLL

IS OF PRINCIPLE OF THE

"DOLL'S THEATORIUM"

(LATEST AMUSEMENT HALL)

Each Doll is 22 inches high, with Bisque head and Articulated Limbs and recites one of the following.

EDISON PHONOGRAPH TOY MANUFACTURING

5 Edison demonstrating his tin-foil phonograph, 1878

were used the artist would have to repeat the performance ten times to produce a total of just 50 cylinders.

One of the most important improvements was made in 1887 when Emile Berliner patented his *gramophone*. Berliner was not satisfied with the to and fro cutting action of the Edison stylus because a deep cut led to a distortion of the sound. He decided to make the stylus move from side to side as it cut the groove. But Berliner had an even more important idea; instead of recording on cylinders, he was going to record on discs. This innovation led to the mass-production of records from one recording. The master recording was made by cutting the side-to-side groove in a wax disc, after which a negative copy or *matrix* was made, with ridges instead of grooves. This, in turn, was used to press many positive copies.

Edison continued to improve his wax-cylinder phonographs and in 1889 he set up a company to make talking dolls. In 1895 he introduced a phonograph powered by a clockwork motor, and by the early years of this century Edison phonographs had become very popular. This popularity did not last for very long because the gramophone, with its mass-produced disc records, was gaining ground. By 1912 Edison had to change to discs, but he retained the up and down movement of the stylus which became known as 'hill and dale' recording. All recordings were still made with a mouthpiece and diaphragm and these were called 'acoustic' recordings.

But music-lovers were demanding better quality than this system could provide. In the 1920s electric recordings were made using microphones and amplifiers. Gramophones powered by electric motors followed and, with the introduction of high-fidelity and stereophonic recording techniques we come to the modern record-player.

14 *Electric Light*

There are three main types of electric light and most of us are regular users of two – bulbs with a filament and fluorescent tubes. The third kind, rarely seen these days, is the arc-lamp which was the earliest practical source of electric light. An arc is really a spark which is kept alight for a long time. To produce an arc two wires from a source of electricity were each connected to a carbon rod or 'electrode'. The electrode ends were brought together and the current switched on. Then the touching ends were separated so that the arc jumped across the gap and increased in brilliance until the gap became too great for the electricity to jump across.

The carbon arc was demonstrated as early as 1810 by the famous scientist Sir Humphry Davy at the Royal Institution in London, but it was of little practical use because there were no machines to produce a steady supply of electricity – Davy used 2000 batteries and his arc lasted only a few minutes. Davy later invented a safety lamp for miners which consisted of an oil lamp with a wick protected by gauze. He refused to patent his lamp, nor would he make any money out of his idea and the Davy lamp became world famous.

During these early years of the nineteenth century, gas lighting was rapidly gaining popularity and electric light remained very much in the background. Then in 1846 W. E. Staite invented a much improved arc-lamp. He improved the purity of the carbon used for the electrodes, and he overcame the problem of the carbon burning away to make an ever-widening gap. He fitted a clockwork mechanism which moved one of the carbon electrodes very slowly towards the other and this compensated for the burning away.

Staite also experimented with metal filament lamps or

bulbs in which a thin metal filament became so hot under the electric current that it glowed brightly enough to give off light. This 'incandescent' filament was fitted inside a glass bulb, but even with most of the air removed it soon burnt away. Here was the major problem to be solved by the future inventor of the light bulb.

Staite exhibited one of his bulbs at a lecture in Sunderland in 1847, and among his audience was a young chemist called Joseph Wilson Swan. Swan was fascinated by the filament problem and spent the next thirty years trying to solve it – of course he invented many other things during this time, including several improvements to photography.

The next important event in the story of electric light had nothing to do with light: in 1870 Z. T. Gramme, a Belgian working in Paris, built the first really practical dynamo capable of generating electricity. At last power was available for the arc-lamp and in 1873 Gramme installed arc-lamps at his Paris factory with great success. Others followed, and in 1875 the Gare du Nord railway station in Paris was similarly lit. In Britain one of the first installations was at the Gaiety Theatre in London during 1878.

But just as the arc-lamp was being accepted, a serious rival emerged – the bulb invented at long last by Joseph Swan. The bulb did not replace the arc-lamp completely, because the arc was very good when great power was needed: for instance sun-ray lamps, theatre lights and cinema projectors all used the carbon-arc until recent times.

The invention of the electric light bulb is another strange story of double invention, with the two inventors separated by the Atlantic Ocean. But before either was successful yet another invention was needed, again not directly connected with light. In 1865 a London-based German scientist called Hermann Sprengel invented a vacuum pump which was far more efficient at removing the air from containers than any

70

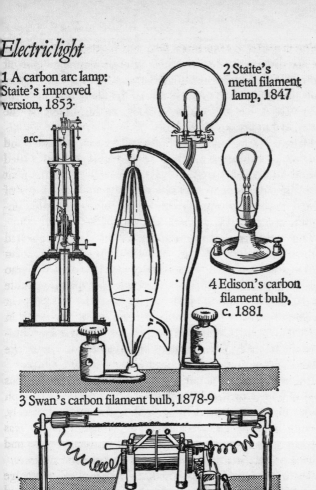

Electric light

1 A carbon arc lamp: Staite's improved version, 1853.

arc—

2 Staite's metal filament lamp, 1847

4 Edison's carbon filament bulb, c. 1881

3 Swan's carbon filament bulb, 1878-9

5 An early experimental fluorescent tube by Alexandre Becquerel, 1857

earlier pump. And ten years later Sir William Crookes improved this pump even further. Now these developments were vital to a bulb inventor because the less air there was inside the bulb, the longer the life of the filament.

In Britain Joseph Swan started by making filaments out of strips of paper coated with carbon in one form or another, and baked in a kiln. He tried charcoal, treacle, tar and many other things during his early experiments around 1850. Success finally came from his experiments of the late 1870s after the invention of the Gramme dynamo and the improved vacuum pump. With the aid of a highly-skilled glass-blower called C. H. Stearn, Swan made a strange slim-looking bulb with a thin carbon filament. But there was a new problem: the inside of the bulb went black when the current was turned on. Swan's hasty experiments led to the vital discovery that this could be avoided by allowing a current to flow through the filament while the air was actually being pumped out of the bulb. All the major problems of the incandescent filament lamp had now been solved and Swan successfully demonstrated his invention to the Newcastle Literary and Philosophical Society on 3rd February, 1879. Swan then set about getting his lamp into production without bothering to take out a patent.

Meanwhile, in the United States, the great inventor Thomas Alva Edison announced in September 1878 that he was going to invent 'a safe, mild, and inexpensive electric light'. So confident were his financial backers that they even founded the Edison Electric Light Company – before he made his invention! The search for a filament started and lasted for about fourteen hectic months. Edison and his staff tried platinum, horsehair, bamboo, grass and tree fibres, and even hairs from their own beards. By October 1879 Edison, like Swan, had produced a bulb with a carbon filament in a vacuum, with the aid of a skilled glass-blower – in this case a man called Ludwig Boehm who produced a bulb shaped more like its modern counterpart. Edison was an experienced inventor and did not waste any time in patenting his bulb, both in America and in Britain. His British patent was dated November 1879 and poor Swan had not yet got around to patenting his bulb. A great legal battle followed and many harsh words were spoken. In 1883 a solution was found: the two companies merged to form the Edison and Swan United Electric Light Company. This company then set about eliminating any opposition.

The incandescent filament bulb was the most important single invention in the story of electric light, but it was not the end of the story. The bulb itself was greatly improved over the years and in the early 1930s coloured mercury and sodium 'discharge' lamps became very popular for street lighting and advertisements. Then in the late 1930s the fluorescent tube was invented and demonstrated at the New York World Fair of 1938. Because the fluorescent tube was more economical than the filament bulb it became very popular during the Second World War, especially in factories where night shifts were being worked. Today the rivalry between the bulb and the tube remains unresolved – both remain popular.

The petrol engine which powers most of the motor cars on our roads today is one of a family of engines called *internal combustion engines*, which are, in turn, part of an even larger group called *heat engines*. A steam engine is also a heat engine, because it needs a fire to power it: heat from the fire turns water into steam, and this is made to do useful work inside a cylinder by moving a circular piston to and fro. The steam engine is a distant relative of the internal combustion engine. They both need heat to power them, but in a steam engine it is supplied by a fire in the boiler – well away from the working cylinder – whereas with an internal combustion engine the heat is generated *inside* the working cylinder. Several early inventors in the seventeeth century thought of this idea, but their source of heat was not very efficient – they tried to explode gunpowder inside a cylinder and thereby move a piston. No successful gunpowder engine emerged, but the idea of an internal combustion engine was born, although two centuries were to pass before a working engine was invented. And for most of this time the steam engine reigned supreme.

When the first successful internal combustion engine was built, it resembled its relative the steam engine in appearance, but of course its method of operation was completely different. The piston was moved inside the cylinder by an explosion – not gunpowder this time but a mixture of gas and air ignited by an electric spark. The inventor of this engine was a French engineer called Etienne Lenoir and his first 'gas engine' ran in 1860. It was an immediate success as a source of power in small factories and workshops, in spite of its high gas consumption. To compensate for this disadvantage, it was a very compact little engine and easy to operate because, unlike the steam engine, it did not have a fire which had to be stoked up hours before the engine was needed.

Several improvements followed to reduce the fuel consumption of the gas engine and increase its power. Probably the most notable was the introduction of an extra 'compression stroke' which compressed the mixture of gas and air before it was ignited. This resulted in a much larger explosion. To achieve this the piston had to make four strokes for each explosion: on the first stroke gas and air were sucked in, on the return stroke they were compressed, on the third stroke the explosion took place and on the final stroke the exhaust gases were forced out.

Not surprisingly this became known as the four-stroke cycle and credit for its invention is usually given to the German engineer Nikolaus Otto of the firm Otto and Langen – it was also called the Otto-cycle. In fairness, some credit should be given to a Frenchman, Alphonse Beau de Rochas, who suggested the idea in 1862, but it was Otto who made it work in 1876. Otto four-stroke gas engines were an immediate success and sold by the thousand all over the world.

Gas engines could drive machinery but they were just not suitable for powering road vehicles because they were so slow-running and needed a gas supply. Gas was normally manufactured at a gas works or by a large gas-producing machine: it was supplied to the engines by a pipe. Obviously a moving vehicle could not be supplied by a pipe so another source of gas was needed. The answer to this problem turned out to be petrol, which is normally a liquid, but can very easily be converted into a vapour. It became clear to several inventors that petrol vapour could replace gas, but it was one thing to have an idea and quite another to make it work successfully. One of the first petrol engines was invented by an Austrian, Siegfried Marcus, who fitted it into a motor car

Petrol engines

Lenoir's gas engine, 1860

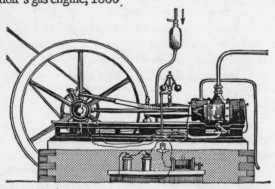

The four-stroke cycle

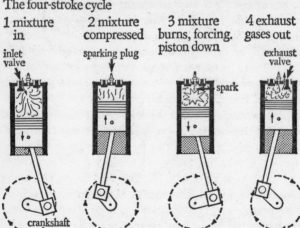

1 mixture in

inlet valve

2 mixture compressed

sparking plug

3 mixture burns, forcing piston down

spark

4 exhaust gases out

exhaust valve

crankshaft

Early petrol-engine vehicles

1 Marcus's car, c. 1875

2 Daimler motorcycle, 1885

3 Benz three-wheeler, 1885

4 Daimler car, 1886

and drove through the streets of Vienna in about 1875. The car was very slow and extremely noisy – in fact the police banned Marcus from the public roads and he appears to have lost interest in motor cars. His car is still preserved in the Vienna Technical Museum.

In 1881 an employee of the firm Otto and Langen left to produce engines of his own design. Gottlieb Daimler, assisted by his friend Wilhelm Maybach, set up a small workshop at Cannstatt in Germany where they worked long hours to produce a high-speed engine. By 1883 they had patented an improved gas engine and by 1885 they had built a compact four-stroke petrol engine. The key to success lay in the *carburettor* which Daimler devised to produce the correct mixture of petrol vapour and air. The engine had a single vertical cylinder and developed only half a horse power but, more important, it rotated at about 700 revolutions per minute, which was very fast by comparison with earlier gas engines.

Daimler offered the engine to his former employers but they turned it down. Little did they realise that this was the forerunner of a new generation of engines which would power motor cars, aeroplanes and boats. Undeterred, Daimler carried on developing his engine and fitted it into a primitive motorcycle which his son Paul demonstrated on 10th November, 1885. In the following year Daimler built his first motor car or 'horseless carriage' – in fact it was a second-hand horse-drawn carriage which Daimler had bought, removed the shafts and fitted with one of his engines.

Meanwhile, in Mannheim not very far away, another German inventor had also invented a petrol-engined vehicle quite independently of Daimler. His name was Karl Benz and in 1885 he built a specially designed three-wheeled vehicle, powered by a horizontal engine between the rear wheels. This engine was not so advanced as Daimler's, for it was much closer to the old slow-speed gas engine design, but it worked and it was reasonably reliable.

By 1886 both these famous inventors had invented a petrol-engined motor car, but their outlook was very different. Benz produced a well-thought-out chassis and fitted an adapted primitive engine, whereas Daimler adapted a primitive chassis and fitted an excellently-designed engine. They must share much of the credit, but with Daimler taking precedence for the invention of the petrol engine and Benz for the motor car. Incidentally, both their cars are preserved in the Deutsches Museum, Munich.

By 1888 motor cars were on sale to the public, but the petrol-engined car was not an immediate success. The railways were a well-established form of transport by the late nineteenth century, whereas cars were expensive and unreliable. Roads were not very good, and of course there were very few garages selling petrol. It was by no means certain that the petrol engine would turn out to be the most successful source of power for road vehicles, because steam cars and electric cars were gaining in popularity. The first speed record of 63.18 kilometres per hour (39.24 miles per hour) was set in 1898 by an electric car and the following five records were all set by electric cars. In 1902 a steam car took the record at 120.85 kilometres per hour (75.06 miles per hour) and this was followed by the first petrol-engined car to hold the record.

In 1903 Henry Ford founded the Ford Motor Company in the United States and his decision to mass-produce petrol-engined cars played a major part in forcing the makers of electric and steam cars out of business and establishing the petrol engine in the dominant position it holds today. But with oil becoming scarce perhaps the old rivals will return in new and improved forms.

When radio was first invented it was called wireless telegraphy, because it was intended as an extension to the existing telegraph service: it would be used to send messages in morse code between two places not linked by a telegraph line. The first patent was granted on 2nd June, 1896, not to one of the eminent scientists who had for many years been studying radiation (later shortened to radio) waves, but to a young Italian called Guglielmo Marconi.

Marconi was only twenty-two years old in 1896 and could perhaps best be described as an enthusiastic amateur inventor. But he had a great advantage over the scientists, who were primarily interested in theories and ideas: he had a flair for picking out the really practical features in other people's discoveries and inventions, and putting these to good use. He was also a good businessman—another rare quality for an inventor.

Guglielmo Marconi was born at Bologna in Italy, the son of a wealthy Italian father and an Irish mother. His mother encouraged his scientific experiments and young Guglielmo was allowed to use part of the top storey of their country villa as a laboratory. These large rooms had, in the past, been used for storing trays of silkworms and here Marconi began his radio experiments in 1894. He studied the works of the great scientists – and it was an impressive list. James Clerk Maxwell had predicted that electromagnetic waves generated by an electrical disturbance, such as a spark, would travel at the speed of light. Twenty years later Heinrich Hertz had demonstrated this *radiation.* He generated a large spark between two metal balls: this was a *transmitter.* The radiation waves travelled through the air to a *receiver* which consisted of a loop with a small gap in it. A spark jumped across this gap every time one was generated by the transmitter. Lord Rutherford, Sir Oliver Lodge, and many other scientists had carried out similar experiments and improved man's understanding of these 'Hertzian waves'.

In Russia, a physicist called Professor A.S. Popov was having some success during 1895. One of his innovations was the use of a suspended wire as an aerial on his receiver. He made several other improvements, and in Russia he is claimed to be the inventor of wireless telegraphy. But he was only one of many inventors involved in this important work and there is little doubt that if one man was responsible for the invention of a successful radio, it was Marconi.

During 1895 Marconi experimented by sending radio signals across the silkworm rooms and soon discovered the advantages of fitting an aerial to both transmitter and receiver. This enabled him to transmit signals from greater distances away from the house altogether. Marconi's brother took the receiver and moved further and further away from the house, waving his handkerchief as a signal each time he picked up the transmission. By September the brothers had increased the distance to such an extent that the receiver was out of sight, so a rifle shot was used to indicate success. Marconi tried to interest the Italian government in his invention, but they were not very helpful – so he travelled to Britain where the family had many friends.

The British Post Office showed considerable interest in Marconi's wireless transmission which he demonstrated from the roof of the London General Post Office, but there was no support from the British Government. Marconi continued to improve his system – especially his aerials – and in 1897 he transmitted a signal about 14 kilometres (8.7 miles) across the Bristol Channel. This success encouraged Marconi and his supporters, so they set up a company called the Wireless Telegraph and Signal Company (in 1900 it became the Marconi Wireless Telegraph Company). The aim of the company was to develop ship-to-shore radio communications, and within a few years they had many successful installations. For instance, in 1898 a radio link was installed between the East Goodwin Lightship and the South Foreland Lighthouse. In the same year a Dublin newspaper called on Marconi's services to arrange a radio transmission covering the Kingstown Regatta; this must have been the first sporting event to be covered by radio. Incidentally, all radio messages at this time had to be sent by morse code — there was no way of transmitting the human voice. Nevertheless, radio was an invaluable form of communication for shipping and for military purposes, as the British troops discovered during the Boer War.

Perhaps Marconi's greatest achievement came in 1901 when he succeeded in sending a radio signal across the Atlantic Ocean. Until then no one was quite sure whether or not radio waves would be shielded by the curvature of the earth. Before he tackled the Atlantic, Marconi thought he had better check this point, so he sent a signal from the Isle of Wight to the Lizard in Cornwall. It worked, and plans for the transatlantic transmission went ahead.

Marconi built one station at Poldhu in Cornwall and another at Cape Cod, Massachusetts. The first aerial at Poldhu consisted of a ring of masts 60 metres (200 feet) high, but these were blown down in a gale. Two wooden masts were hastily erected and a fan-like aerial fitted between them. By November 1901 everything was ready: then the Cape Cod aerial was blown down! The transmitter at Poldhu was working well so Marconi decided to change his plans and set up a new receiving station a little nearer.

He set sail with two of his assistants for Newfoundland, having left instructions at Poldhu for the letter 'S' (three dots) to be transmitted at certain times during the day. Marconi could not wait for aerial masts to be built; instead he tried to suspend an aerial wire from a balloon, but this was

Radio

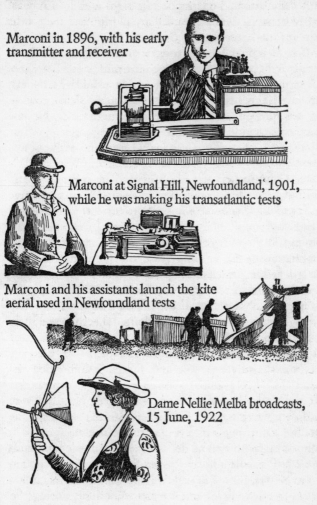

Marconi in 1896, with his early transmitter and receiver

Marconi at Signal Hill, Newfoundland, 1901, while he was making his transatlantic tests

Marconi and his assistants launch the kite aerial used in Newfoundland tests

Dame Nellie Melba broadcasts, 15 June, 1922

unmanageable. Next he tried a kite and lost the first one. The second attempt was more successful and a 152-metre (500-foot) aerial was suspended from the kite: they were ready for the experiment. On 12th December, 1901, at 12.30 p.m. Marconi and his assistants listened intently to their receiver, and sure enough they heard a signal – three dots at regular intervals. Many people would not believe Marconi's claim, but within a few months complete messages were recorded on ships up to 2400 kilometres (1500 miles) from the transmitter at Poldhu.

Radio had come a long way in five years and Marconi was still only twenty-seven years old. The Marconi Wireless Telegraph Company continued to expand its operations and carry out research into new developments. The radio valve (or *thermionic diode* valve to be more correct) was invented in 1904 by one of Marconi's collaborators, John Ambrose Fleming. The valve greatly improved both transmitters and receivers during the ensuing years. But the transmission of speech was the principal target for radio inventors during the early years of the twentieth century and success came very slowly. As early as 1900 one of Edison's former assistants, Reginald Fessenden, transmitted speech over a short distance, and in 1906 he transmitted a programme of music and poetry. Many other inventors struggled with the twofold problem of increasing the range and improving the quality of the reception.

It took a very long time to overcome these difficulties, and broadcasting to the public did not begin until the 1920s. The Marconi Company set up an experimental station at Chelmsford in 1920 and in the same year a commercial station at Pittsburgh in the United States commenced regular operations. The BBC started regular transmissions on 14th November, 1922, and services around the world grew very rapidly once the breakthrough had been made.

84

17　*The Zip Fastener*

There are many inventions which we accept, yet rarely consider how they work or how they were invented. The zip fastener is one of these. It is such a simple thing – once you have seen it work – that it is hard to imagine the trouble it gave its inventors. There were really two main inventors: Whitcomb L. Judson who invented an unsuccessful version, and Gideon Sundback who produced the zip fastener as we know it.

During the nineteenth century, getting dressed was a tedious business, especially for women, because clothes were fastened by rows of buttons, hooks and eyes, or laces. High buttoned boots were very fashionable, but to do them up demanded patience and some skill with a buttonhook! It was this particular problem that, in about 1890, attracted the attention of a Chicago engineer called Whitcomb L. Judson. He designed a 'slide fastener' (the name 'zip fastener' came later) which consisted of hooks and eyes. In appearance each side of the fastener resembled a chain with the links consisting alternately of hooks and rings. As a slide was moved up the fastener, the hook on one side engaged in the ring on the other side. It was a brilliant idea and in 1893 Judson was granted a patent. Together with a business associate, Colonel Lewis Walker, Judson set up a company in Chicago and the slide fastener went into production. Alas, they ran into trouble: the fastener was too complicated to be made by machines, and it had an unfortunate tendency to spring open – to the embarrassment of the wearer!

By 1905 Judson had designed a new fastener which could more easily be made by machines. He still used the hook and eye idea, but this time he put all the hooks on one side of the

The zip fastener

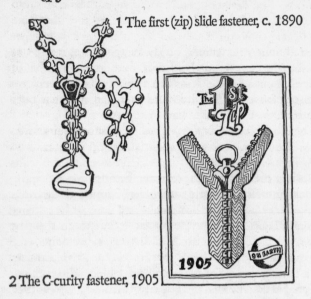

1 The first (zip) slide fastener, c. 1890

2 The C-curity fastener, 1905

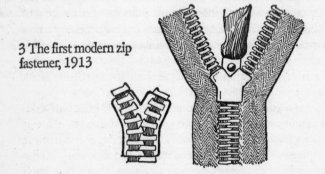

3 The first modern zip
fastener, 1913

fastener and all the eyes on the other. It was easier to manufacture because the hooks and eyes were just clamped on to the edge of a fabric tape and not made up into the more complicated chains of the earlier fastener. The new fastener appeared under the name *C-curity*. Despite its name, it was anything but secure and still had the annoying habit of coming undone. Clothing manufacturers were not very enthusiastic about the improved fastener and its main sales came from door-to-door pedlars.

A new approach was needed, so the company employed Gideon Sundback, a young Swedish electrical engineer who had emigrated to the United States. After several years' work Sundback produced his first fastener, but this too was unreliable in use and the company was on the verge of bankruptcy. By 1912 Sundback had invented a hookless fastener which looked promising: it did not spring open, but on the other hand it wore out very rapidly. A few refinements were made and in 1913 Sundback patented his hookless fastener which had the interlocking teeth of the modern zip fastener. The individual teeth were clamped to flexible tapes and fed together through a carefully shaped slider. The slider curved both lines of teeth and this had the effect of opening up the gaps between the teeth so that they could be meshed alternately one into the other. Once the lines were straight again the teeth were locked together. Sundback's great invention was essentially very simple – far simpler than Judson's hook and eye fastener.

The new fastener went into production and here too Sundback had used his inventive genius to design efficient machines for stamping out the identical teeth and attaching them to the tapes. Unfortunately, the clothing manufacturers were still reluctant to incorporate fasteners in their designs – perhaps they were still worried by the earlier designs' tendency to unfasten! However, a breakthrough was made towards the end of the First World War when a contractor making flying suits for the United States Navy fitted them with Sundback's fasteners. A further boost came in 1923 when they were fitted to the very popular galoshes made by the B. F. Goodrich Company, and it was here that the fasteners were christened *zippers*. The other popular name *zip fastener* dates from about the same time: an enterprising salesman demonstrating the fastener is reputed to have said 'Zip, it's open, zip it's closed'.

During the late 1920s and early 1930s zip fasteners became popular in many parts of the world – they were even incorporated in dresses designed by the fashion houses of Paris and New York. Unlike some inventors, Gideon Sundback did benefit financially from his invention, for both he and Colonel Walker became millionaires.

18 *Television*

Television was invented twice, but unlike many double inventions, the two solutions to the same problem were completely different. One was a relatively simple invention, often described as mechanical television, while the other made use of electronics and was very much more complex.

The story of television begins during the mid-nineteenth century, when inventors were trying to send still pictures along telegraph wires. The Abbé Castelli, an Italian priest living in France, sent shadowy pictures between Paris and Lyons in 1862. George Carey of Boston went a stage further and suggested an idea for transmitting a moving picture in 1875. He proposed to divide the subject into tiny elements and then transmit details of each element simultaneously. This needed a separate circuit for each element, a fact which made it far too complicated. In about 1880 several inventors came up with an idea to simplify the operation: the elements would be *scanned* one after the other and then transmitted over a single circuit. The speed of the operation would deceive the human eye into registering just one picture or *frame* for each scanning operation. One frame would follow another so rapidly that again the human eye would be deceived, this time into seeing moving pictures – just as a ciné film has separate frames flashing on the screen so quickly that the eye thinks it is seeing continuous movement.

This important idea was converted into a practical experiment by a German inventor called Paul Nipkow who devised a very ingenious method of scanning. He made a rotating disc pierced by a number of small holes cut on a line spiralling towards the centre; each hole scanned a separate line across the subject. Light and dark areas of the subject would be scanned and 'seen' by a photoelectric cell: a device which converts light into electricity. Then the electrical 'message' could be transmitted to a receiver and converted into a picture. Although Nipkow did not succeed in transmitting a picture, his idea was good, and was used by later inventors.

At the turn of the century there were a number of inventions leading to the rival electronic system. In 1897 Ferdinand Braun of Germany developed the cathode-ray tube which could convert electric signals into a visible form. In 1904 Ambrose Fleming invented the diode radio valve, and two years later the American inventor Lee de Forest improved it with a 'grid' – which made amplification possible. A great step forward was made in 1907, when a Russian scientist called Boris Rosing built a television system. His camera incorporated mirrors on a rotating drum which acted as a scanner, and this was combined with Braun's cathode-ray tube at the receiver end. Rosing did manage to transmit and receive some simple geometric shapes with his primitive system. In 1908 the Scottish inventor Alan Archibald Campbell-Swinton outlined a television system with cathode-ray tubes at both camera and receiver, and his ideas were remarkably close to the final electronic system. But at this stage it was only an idea and practical television was still a long way ahead.

The man who demonstrated the first real television pictures was another Scottish inventor, John Logie Baird. In the 1920s, after several years' work, he invented a primitive mechanical system which transmitted a flickering picture over a distance of a metre or so. Baird used a rotating disc, developed from the one invented by Nipkow, in both his camera and his receiver. At first he only obtained shadowy images, but on 2nd October, 1925, he achieved his first clear picture – the head of 'Bill', his ventriloquist's dummy. On 26th January, 1926, he gave a public demonstration to forty distinguished members of the Royal Institution.

These early pictures were very crude by modern standards: the picture was formed on only 30 lines (today we use 625) and it repeated at about ten times a second – which meant it flickered badly. The picture was very dim and smaller in size than a pound note. Baird formed the Baird Television Development Company, and in 1929 he combined with the BBC to broadcast the first daily television programmes.

Television was a popular novelty, especially in 1931 when the Derby was televised for the first time, but a much better picture was needed before it could be rated as entertainment. Baird rushed ahead with many other ambitious projects such as transatlantic television, colour television, large-screen television and even stereoscopic television. It was not until 1933 that he set about improving his 30-line picture by increasing the number of lines. By 1935 his new system was ready – but so were his rivals with an electronic television.

The Russian pioneer of electronic television, Boris Rosing, had a bright young student working for him from 1910 to 1912. This student, Vladimir Zworykin, emigrated to the United States as a penniless refugee in 1919 and became one of the most important figures in television history. In 1923 he patented a very special cathode-ray tube for use in a television camera. It used an electron beam for scanning, very much faster than the rotating disc of the mechanical system. This *iconoscope* was an outstanding idea, but it needed a great deal of development before it would work.

The Radio Corporation of America (RCA) provided Zworykin with men and money, and in 1928 he was able to demonstrate his invention. By 1932, RCA had developed an all-electric 120-line television system incorporating Zworykin's iconoscope camera and an improved cathode-ray tube for the receiver. However they were not alone in the field of

91

Television

1 Nipkow scanning disc

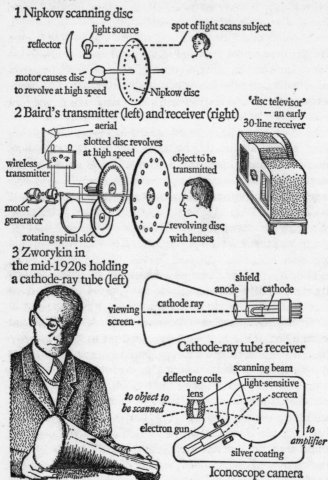

reflector

light source

spot of light scans subject

motor causes disc to revolve at high speed

Nipkow disc

2 Baird's transmitter (left) and receiver (right)

'disc televisor' — an early 30-line receiver

aerial

slotted disc revolves at high speed

wireless transmitter

object to be transmitted

motor

generator

rotating spiral slot

revolving disc with lenses

3 Zworykin in the mid-1920s holding a cathode-ray tube (left)

shield

anode

cathode

viewing screen→

cathode ray

Cathode-ray tube receiver

scanning beam

deflecting coils

light-sensitive screen

lens

to object to be scanned

electron gun

to amplifier

silver coating

Iconoscope camera

electronic television, for in 1927 a young, self-taught inventor working secretly in a small laboratory in the United States, also invented a reasonably successful system. His name was Philo T. Farnsworth and he was backed by the Philco Corporation. His camera was nowhere near as good as Zworykin's but his patents covered many aspects of electronic television. So there ensued a long-drawn-out legal battle between RCA and Farnsworth's company which was not resolved until 1941.

Meanwhile, in Britain more practical events were taking place. Electrical and Musical Industries Ltd (EMI) realised the possibilities of Zworykin's system and in 1931 set up a research team under Isaac Shoenberg. This team developed a camera with an improved version of the iconoscope known as the 'Emitron' camera tube, and for the receiver they developed an improved high-vacuum cathode-ray tube. In 1934 a joint Marconi-EMI company was established and very promising results were achieved. Britain now had two successful television systems: Baird's mechanical one and the Marconi-EMI electronic system. A Television Committee set up by the government made a thorough examination of the situation and in January 1935 recommended that a competition should be held to decide between the two systems. The BBC would broadcast using Baird or Marconi-EMI equipment on alternate weeks. The world's first regular service of high-definition television took place on 2nd November, 1936, from Alexandra Palace in North London. Baird's equipment operated on 240 lines but was much less adaptable than the electronic system which used 405 lines. The competition did not last very long and in February 1937 it was announced that the BBC would adopt the Marconi-EMI electronic system. Baird never gave up hope of a revival but he was beaten by a superior system, the heart of which was the very fine Emitron camera tube.

19 *Catseyes and Biros*

The catseyes down the middle of a road and the biro ball-point pen are very different, yet as inventions they had many similarities. Each was the idea of one man and each became very popular after a reluctant start; strangely enough both were assisted along the road to success by the Second World War. They were such simple ideas that, once seen, it is hard to imagine why they were not invented sooner. In fact there were earlier attempts, but in each case the brilliance of the final invention was its complete reliability.

Percy Shaw is not a name most people would include in a list of great inventors, yet this Yorkshire road engineer invented the catseye, which has made driving in poor visibility so much easier, and must have saved many lives. Percy was the son of a labourer who struggled to support a family of fourteen. He himself built up a flourishing business repairing roads – a job which involved travelling about West Yorkshire in all weathers. Fog and smog were frequent hazards and one of the few ways of staying on the road was to follow the tramlines – for most of the Yorkshire towns had trams during the 1930s.

On one particularly bad night in 1933 Percy Shaw was driving home along a dangerous road from Queensbury to Halifax: it was so bad that he could not even see the tramlines. Only two things could he see clearly, the eyes of a cat sitting on a fence and some reflectors on a sign beside the road. 'I thought it would be a good idea to bring them down to road level' he said later, and this he did. After a year of experiments he had fifty of his reflecting road studs or 'catseyes' installed at a dangerous crossroads near Bradford.

In 1935 Shaw set up a company called Reflecting Road

Studs Ltd, to manufacture his catseyes, and two years later the Ministry of Transport installed ten different varieties of reflecting road studs along an 8-km (5-mile) stretch of road. Within two years all had broken or stopped reflecting except Percy Shaw's catseyes, which were still in perfect condition. What was the secret of their success?

The catseye design consists of a metal frame which is sunk into the surface of the road, and inside this frame is a rubber pad. Two 'eyes' facing in each direction are embedded in the pad. The design of the glass eye is very important and although each eye is made in a single piece of glass it consists of two parts, a lens at the front and a silvered mirror at the rear. The mirror is curved and this gathers the incoming light so that it is reflected back through the lens in a concentrated beam. Incidentally, a cat has a white covering on the retina of its eyes which acts as a mirror and reflects light back to the source in a similar way, so the name *catseye* is very appropriate. But Percy Shaw had yet another ingenious idea which he built into his invention. As a car wheel runs over the catseye, the rubber pad containing the eyes sinks down into the metal housing. As the eyes move down they are wiped clean by part of the rubber pad – rather like a windscreen wiper. Now this simple operation made all the difference to the success of Shaw's catseyes because without it they would have been coated in dirt in no time.

There was no doubt about the success of Shaw's catseyes, then in 1939 the Second World War started. This was a great boost for sales because a blackout was imposed to prevent enemy aircraft seeing their targets clearly. There were no street lights, so catseyes were an ideal way of guiding drivers in the dark. What is more, because the catseye reflected all the light back to its source, none strayed upwards for aircraft to see. Percy Shaw became very wealthy, yet he continued to live alone in the house where he

Catseyes and biros

Catseyes are anchored into the road surface

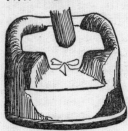

The Catseye: a strong iron case holds a rubber pad containing the eyes. When a vehicle passes over, the eyes are pushed down into the rubber, which wipes them clean

The first ball-point pen: Laszlo and Georg Biro's patent drawing. The end of their pen unscrewed for filling

Percy Shaw's patent drawing shows the two 'eyes' embedded in their rubber casing

was born near Halifax. In appearance he resembled a retired labourer and his house had neither carpets nor curtains, but he did have four television sets. Percy Shaw was a remarkable individual – a lone inventor to whom all motorists owe a debt of gratitude.

The ball-point pen was invented by a Hungarian journalist called László Biró with the help of his brother Georg who was a chemist. (The accents are usually omitted in the English version of their name). Laszlo Biro was proof-reading a magazine in Budapest during 1938 and two aspects of his work caused him to stop and think: he had to pause from time to time to fill his fountain pen and he had to wait for the ink to dry, or blot it carefully. As a result of these deliberations he made a ball-point pen and with the help of his brother, the chemist, produced a suitable quick-drying ink.

Before the brothers could develop their idea the Second World War broke out. They escaped from Hungary to Paris and later went on to Argentina where they settled and resumed work on their pen. By about 1943 the new 'biro' pen was working well; the ink flowed freely yet did not flood, and it dried quickly. The Biros' attention to detail had produced a winner, which was far superior to earlier ball-point designs dating back to the 1880s.

In 1943 an English businessman called Henry Martin was visiting Argentina and he was very impressed by Biro's invention, realising that it would be of value to the Royal Air Force. Normal fountain pens cannot be used at high altitudes because the outside air pressure drops below the pressure of the air trapped inside the rubber ink-container – and ink floods out. Biro's pen did not suffer from this complaint which made it ideal for navigators and other aircrew flying at high altitudes. Martin acquired the right to make the pens in Britain, and production for the RAF began in

1944. Early in the following year commercial sales commenced in the Argentinian capital, Buenos Aires.

But Biro had not taken sufficient care with his patents. A salesman from Chicago called Milton Reynolds bought some and returned to the United States where he rapidly put a slightly modified version into mass-production. This too was a great success: it was issued to United States servicemen and at a New York store it was advertised as the 'first pen that writes underwater'! Despite the fact that it was relatively expensive, it sold by the thousand. The Miles-Martin Pen Company was also very successful selling biros in Britain and by 1949 sales of ball-points outstripped those of fountain pens. In 1958 the first very cheap throw-away ball-point pen went on sale in Britain, having been developed by the French company Bic. These sold by the million and have become a part of our way of life.

20 Man-made Materials: Acrilan to Xylonite

In the world of chemistry most materials have emerged as the result of a discovery rather than an invention. For instance, oxygen, coal gas, rubber, salt and alcohol were all made from natural materials found in one form or another. But during the last hundred years a whole new range of materials has become available, and these are entirely man-made. They can be very different in appearance and use, ranging from the recent synthetic fibres such as acrilan back to the early plastics like celluloid (Xylonite is a trade name for celluloid). Many man-made materials have resulted from experiments to find a cheap substitute for an existing material. One of the first plastics resulted from just this situation during the 1860s, when Alexander Parkes of Birmingham was attempting to produce synthetic horn – a popular material for decorative items at that time. Parkes demonstrated his new material at the 1862 International Exhibition held in London, where he showed that it could be used to make a whole range of things from doorknobs to hand mirrors. By 1866 it was in production and had been named *parkesine*: in technical terms it was a 'thermoplastic' material which was produced from nitrocellulose, camphor and alcohol.

A very similar material was invented a few years later in the United States by John Wesley Hyatt assisted by his brother Isaiah. Hyatt called his material *celluloid*. In about 1870 Hyatt set out to win a prize of $10 000 offered by a New York firm to anyone who could invent a substitute for ivory in the manufacture of billiard balls. He produced a very good thermoplastic material based on his celluloid formula which included nitrocellulose (this is also known as guncotton – a powerful explosive). The billiard balls worked well except for two faults: if a lighted cigar touched a ball it went up in flames, and when two balls collided rather violently, they sometimes exploded! One saloon proprietor complained to Hyatt saying that the noise itself was not the problem, it was the reaction by his customers – every man in the saloon instantly drew his gun!

The next important man-made material was *bakelite*, invented by Leo Hendrik Baekeland in 1909. This was a 'thermosetting' material which differed from the earlier thermoplastics such as celluloid, and this difference was most important. The celluloid-type (thermoplastic) materials could not withstand heat: when heated they just turned soft or plastic. Bakelite (thermosetting), on the other hand, was formed under heat plus pressure and once 'cured' it was unaffected by changes of temperature. It could also resist many chemicals.

Baekeland was born in Belgium and became a professor of chemistry and physics at Bruges. He moved to the United States where he invented a new type of photographic printing paper and this provided him with enough money to start a series of experiments with synthetic resins. Others had tried to produce plastics in this way but failed: the secret of Baekeland's success was his three-stage curing process. The Bakelite Corporation was founded in 1910 and as the company slogan said, bakelite was 'The material with a thousand uses'. For example there were bakelite telephones, gearwheels, salt cellars, electrical fittings and picnic cups. Incidentally, early plastic items made in parkesine or even bakelite are now collectors' pieces and much sought after.

For many years chemists had been trying to produce a transparent foil and although several attempts nearly succeeded, the real breakthrough occurred in 1912 when

Jacques Edwin Brandenberger invented *cellophane*. Brandenberger was born in Switzerland but worked in France as a dye chemist. A company called La Cellophane was set up and the new material went into production in France. However, it had only a limited success, for it was not waterproof.

After the First World War the American chemical company E. I. du Pont de Nemours acquired the right to manufacture cellophane in the United States, and production began in 1924. The du Pont company set out to produce a waterproof version of cellophane, and by 1927 the problem had been solved by two of their employees, W. H. Church and K. E. Prindle. They found a way of applying a very thin waterproof coating on both sides of the cellophane. This improvement boosted sales dramatically as cellophane could now be used to wrap cigarettes, biscuits, sweets and groceries.

Another transparent plastic was being developed at about the same time, but this one was rigid and more like glass. It was known chemically as polymerised methyl methacrylate and we know it as *perspex*. There were many contributors towards the success of this very useful material, which is much simpler to shape than glass and does not break so easily. The patent for perspex was granted in 1933 to Dr Rowland Hill of Imperial Chemical Industries (ICI) and later a licence was granted to the du Pont company by ICI.

In 1933 another important material was invented by ICI but at the time its importance was not recognised. Two employees, R. O. Gibson and E. W. Fawcett, carried out an experiment with ethylene and benzaldehyde which produced a white wax-like substance. This was a polymer of ethylene or as it later became known, *polythene*.

The first practical use for this new material was to insulate underwater cables. Regular production was started in September 1939 and most of the output went to produce cables or components for airborne radar equipment. When the War ended in 1945 polythene was used to make a host of household articles – starting with washing-up bowls.

In the years since 1945 there have been many new plastic materials sold under an even larger number of trade names, but one group of materials has a history going back into the nineteenth century – man-made fibres. The first man-made fibres were made from wood pulp and patented in 1855 by a Swiss chemist, George Audemars: they were of no practical use and quickly forgotten. The idea was resurrected in 1883 by Joseph Swan when he was looking for a suitable material from which to make filaments for his electric light bulbs. Swan forcéd nitrocellulose through tiny holes and into acetic acid to produce fine threads. His wife crocheted small mats using the new threads and these were exhibited at an Inventions Exhibition in 1885. Swan named his new material 'artificial silk', but he did not develop the operation as a commercial venture. This was done in France by Comte Hilaire de Chardonnet who set up a factory and manufactured artificial silk under the name *rayon*. An improved yarn called *viscose rayon* was invented in Britain during 1898 by C. H. Stearn and C. S. Cross, and this could be woven into cloth. Production began in 1905, and by 1910 a factory in Germany was producing the first artificial silk stockings.

Although rayon was a man-made yarn, it was manufactured from fibrous natural materials such as wood pulp. The first completely synthetic yarn – made from benzene, oxygen, nitrogen and hydrogen – was produced in 1937 and called simply *nylon*.

The name nylon was chosen by the American du Pont company who had developed this important new material in their laboratories. A team of scientists under the direction of Dr Wallace H. Carothers worked for ten years before perfecting the formula for 'nylon 66', as they called it. The first

102

Man-made materials

Early plastic objects: *left to right*, mug, hand mirror, clock and cruet set

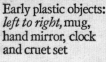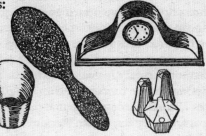

Artificial silk dress and petticoat of the 1930s

Making nylon: nylon is formed by a chemical reaction between two substances. The nylon thread is drawn out of the beaker on a glass rod

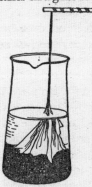

commercially produced nylon appeared in the United States during 1938 and went on sale as toothbrush bristles. During the following year nylon yarn went into production, and the American stocking manufacturers waited eagerly for the exciting new material. They all agreed to wait and launch their new brands on the same day: so on 15th May, 1940, nylon stockings made their formidable debut.

Nylon was first produced in Britain during 1941 but, due to the War, all the output went to the armed forces – mainly for parachute fabric. Nylon stockings came to Britain with the American forces and were a highly-prized commodity. The first British nylons went on sale in December 1946.

It has been said that no other invention has had such a revolutionary effect on women's lives. After nylon stockings a whole host of new nylon products emerged: underwear, clothing, sheets, carpets, artificial fur and even saucepan scourers. Other popular synthetic fibres were invented, starting with *terylene*, a polyester fibre, in 1941. This was followed by *orlon*, a soft acrylic fibre, which was patented in 1946, and since then there have been many other fibres manufactured and sold under numerous brand names. Man-made materials play such a large part in normal, everyday life that they must surely represent one of the least thought-about great inventions.

Towards the end of the Second World War, jet fighters made their first appearance in the air above Europe and during the 1950s the first jet airliners arrived on the world's airways. The jet age had started, but the invention of the jet engine happened a long time before. The idea of using the 'thrust' from a jet goes back to the first century A.D. when Hero of Alexandria made a device called an Aeolipile. This was a sphere filled with steam which rotated when the steam escaped through two small jets (the lawn sprinkler works on the same principle, but with jets of water). The aeolipile was no more than a toy, but, although he did not realise it, Hero had invented the first steam turbine.

There were several attempts to use jet-thrust during the eighteenth century, and in 1787 an American engineer, James Rumsey, actually built a jet-propelled boat powered by a steam engine which pumped a jet of water out of the stern. This was not a success, and anyway it hardly qualifies as a jet engine because to most people a jet engine means the type of engine used to power today's airliners, fighters and bombers. The modern jet engine belongs to a whole family of engines called *gas turbines*.

In a gas turbine, air is drawn into the engine and compressed by an air compressor; then it passes to a combustion section into which fuel is sprayed and ignited. The fuel burns fiercely and produces hot gases at high temperature and pressure. These gases emerge from the rear of the engine as a jet. However, before emerging they pass through a turbine (a high-speed windmill), and this turbine drives the compressor. If a larger turbine is fitted, it can be used to drive a propeller in addition to the compressor, and this is called a turbo-prop or prop-jet engine.

When the gas turbine was first introduced in 1905, it was not intended for use in aircraft but as an industrial engine. Most of the power from its hot gases was absorbed by a large turbine which drove machinery. It became known as a gas turbine to distinguish it from the steam turbine which had been in use for some years. The hot gases were quite a problem because, in the early days, there were no metals which could stand up to their heat.

The aircraft jet engine was invented quite separately in Britain and in Germany during the 1930s and 1940s under conditions of great secrecy. Britain was the first to design, build and test-run a jet engine on the ground, but Germany was the first to fly a jet aircraft. The British inventor was a flying instructor in the RAF called Frank Whittle. The idea of adapting the gas turbine engine to power an aircraft seemed a logical development to Whittle, and in 1929 he tried to persuade the Air Ministry that his engine was feasible. They turned it down, but Whittle patented the design in January 1930. A few years later he went to Cambridge University to study engineering and carry out research. A new company called Power Jets Ltd was set up to help him develop his jet engine, and by 1937 Whittle and his colleagues had built the world's first jet engine. On 12th April it was run for the first time in a 'test bed'.

The German inventor was a young engineer called Hans Pabst von Ohain who worked in collaboration with the aircraft designer Professor Ernst Heinkel. In September 1937 von Ohain's engine ran for the first time. Heinkel had already built an aeroplane powered by a rocket motor, so the job of producing an aeroplane powered by a jet engine was no great problem. On 27th August, 1939, test pilot Erich Warsitz climbed into the cockpit of the diminutive Heinkel

He 178, started the noisy engine and took off. The jet age had started. But it ended again almost immediately, for when the Second World War began only a few days later, Hitler stopped the test-flying. He wanted all the aircraft industry's efforts put into the production of existing designs in the hope of winning the war as quickly as possible.

Meanwhile in Britain, Air Ministry officials saw Whittle's jet engine running in its test bed, and although they were still a little apprehensive they gave financial support. In March 1938 an order was placed for a new engine to power an experimental aircraft specially designed to take the new jet engine. This aircraft was called the Gloster E.28/39, and it made its first flight on 15th May, 1941, with Flight Lieutenant P. E. G. Sayer at the controls, although it had made a very short hop previously during taxiing trials. The engine on this historic flight was a Whittle W.I. fitted with a centrifugal air compressor, ten combustion chambers and a turbine to drive the compressor. Both aircraft and engine are preserved in the Science Museum in London. As tests continued they demonstrated that the jet engine became more efficient at high speeds and greater altitudes, whereas the conventional piston engine became less efficient under these conditions. These facts had been Whittle's argument from the beginning, but it had been a long struggle to overcome both the technical difficulties and the lack of interest in some official circles.

The first aeroplane to fly using a jet engine was undoubtedly the German Heinkel He 178. However, the Heinkel's engine was not developed for production aircraft, whereas many of the early British and American military jets were powered by engines based on Whittle's design. These engines had a very high fuel consumption, so they were not suitable for airliners, which had to carry a large number of passengers over long distances – and make a

The jet engine

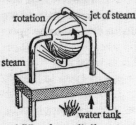

rotation

jet of steam

steam

water tank

1 Hero's aeolipile

2 The jet engine

pure jet

turbo-prop

A. gear box
B. compressor
C. combustion chamber
D. turbine
E. jet-pipe
F. jet

3 The first jet aircraft: Heinkel He 178

4 The first jet airliner service, 1952 Comet, from London to Johannesburg

profit. The engine designers improved the performance of their jet engines during the later 1940s and early 1950s and on 2nd May, 1952, a Comet took off from London bound for Johannesburg on the first regular airline service to be operated by a jet airliner.

22 *Nuclear Power*

The invention of nuclear power is one of the most complex and controversial inventions in man's long history. Scientists from Britain, Denmark, France, Germany, Ireland, Japan, Russia and the United States all contributed to the success of the project, and a list of their names would read like a *Who's Who* of the scientific world. The world's first full-scale nuclear power station to produce electricity on a commercial scale was opened in 1956. This was the Calder Hall Power Station, built on the coast of Cumbria in the north of England. Like most other conventional power stations the electricity at Calder Hall was actually produced by generators – in much the same way as a bicycle dynamo generates electricity. Of course power-station generators are very large, and each one is driven by an engine or *turbine*.

In hydro-electric power stations the turbines are driven by water power, but in most other power stations steam turbines are used. High-pressure steam enters the steam turbine and passes through a large number of blades mounted around the edge of a disc – rather like a windmill with many arms. After passing through the first disc, the steam goes on to a second and many more discs all of which are fixed to one shaft. The shaft is driven round at a high speed and this in turn drives the generator. In a conventional power station, the steam is produced in a boiler which is fired by coal, gas or oil, but in a nuclear power station the steam is produced by a nuclear *reactor*. This highly sophisticated device is therefore doing little more than a simple kettle – boiling water to make steam!

The nuclear reactor at Calder Hall uses uranium as a fuel. As a rough guide, one kilogramme of uranium is equivalent to 10,000 kilogrammes of coal. Deep inside the thick protective walls of the reactor, atomic energy is released by splitting the core, or *nucleus* of uranium atoms. The great heat generated by this reaction is absorbed by carbon dioxide gas, which is pumped through the reactor to keep it cool. This kind of reactor was therefore called a *gas-cooled reactor*. (Later designs used other coolants including water and liquid metals, such as sodium.) The heated carbon dioxide gas is taken from the reactor and passed into a large heat-exchanger where its heat is used to convert water into steam. The cooled gas returns to the reactor, while the steam is led away to drive the turbines.

The energy in a nuclear power station depends on splitting an atom, and many scientists were involved in this work, but the man who invented the first atomic reactor was an Italian called Enrico Fermi who was working in the United States when he achieved success in 1942. The atom had been 'smashed' by Ernest Rutherford as early as 1919 but in his experiments Rutherford always used more energy to split the nucleus of an atom than he generated from the splitting. A major step towards the release of atomic energy came just before the Second World War when two German scientists made an accidental discovery. Otto Hahn and Fritz Strassmann were working with uranium and hoping to produce heavier elements, but to their surprise the result of their experiment was lighter material. The mystery of the missing matter was solved by two other German scientists called Lise Meitner and Otto Frisch who were working in Sweden. They showed that the nucleus of the uranium atom had been split into lighter elements, and the missing mass had been converted into energy – atomic energy. A method making this reaction continuous and self-sustaining was needed; consequently the United States government gathered together the greatest concentration of scientific brains

Nuclear power

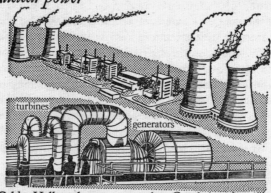

1 Calder Hall nuclear power station, Cumbria: *(above)* general view, *(below)* the turbo-generators

2 Simplified diagram of a gas-cooled reactor

3 The first nuclear reactor Chicago 1942

4 Enrico Fermi

ever to tackle a single project – one of these scientists was Enrico Fermi.

Fermi was born in Rome in 1901, and by 1927 he had become Professor of Theoretical Physics at Rome University. By 1938 he was awarded a Nobel Prize for his work on nuclear research. But Fermi was discontented with the Fascist government in Italy, and after the Nobel ceremony in Stockholm he went to the United States. He carried on his research at Columbia University, where he built a small nuclear reactor or, as it was called at the time, an *atomic pile*. It was completed in 1941 but it turned out to be too small to sustain a continuous reaction.

Towards the end of 1941 Fermi and his team of scientists moved to the University of Chicago and set about building a new 'pile' – in a squash court! Uranium was the nuclear fuel, but Fermi introduced blocks of graphite into the pile to act as a *moderator* and control the rate of the reaction. This was important because it would have been very dangerous if the self-sustaining reaction had got out of control.

At 3.45 p.m. on 2nd December, 1942, Fermi's pile was started up – it worked. A coded message was sent out, 'The Italian Navigator has entered the new world'.

Fermi's pile was the first nuclear reactor, but equally important was the fact that the reaction could be controlled: the reactor could be started and stopped at will. It was the ancestor of all nuclear weapons and nuclear power stations, and a great scientific invention. But the final verdict on its benefit, or otherwise, to mankind will be decided in the future.

23 *The Computer*

When we use the word 'computer' we are usually referring to an electronic digital computer – the most common variety in use today. A dictionary definition helps by naming some of the other varieties: 'calculator: mechanical, electric or electronic machine for carrying out complex calculations'. Mechanical calculators go back some 5000 years to the bead counting-frame or abacus. More advanced mechanical calculators were produced many years later and eventually these were powered by electricity. The invention of the thermionic (or radio) valve made the electronic computer possible and it appeared in two forms: a digital machine and an analogue machine.

The digital computer works with numbers or letters, and is really just a super-efficient high-speed calculator which can add and subtract, multiply and divide. An analogue computer can solve more advanced mathematical problems in which many variables can affect the answer and the solution may involve differential and integral calculus. One example of the early use of an analogue computer was to predict the behaviour of an aircraft in flight: now such computers are used in ground simulators which reconstruct conditions similar to flying conditions, in order to train pilots without the expense of flying.

One of the inventions which led to the digital computer was, strangely enough, a special kind of loom for weaving intricate patterns. In the early nineteenth century a French inventor called Joseph-Marie Jacquard built a loom in which the warp (lengthways) threads were controlled by a set of cards mounted above the loom. Holes punched in these cards dictated which threads were lifted above the shuttle, and this action controlled the pattern.

A very ingenious English inventor called Charles Babbage adapted these punched cards to feed information into his *analytical engine*, which he started to build in 1835. Plungers passed through holes in the cards and operated the intricate mechanism. The machine had two basic components: a storage unit or 'memory', and a calculating section – just like a modern computer. It was to be powered by steam – but despite many years' work, and the expenditure of thousands of pounds of Babbage's and government money, it was never finished. In order to operate successfully, the highly complex mechanism of plungers, levers and gears had to be manufactured to an extremely high standard of accuracy: unfortunately the machine tools available at the time were just not capable of such a standard.

Towards the end of the nineteenth century Herman Hollerith, a statistician, was working on the results of a population census in the United States. The census was held every ten years, but it took almost ten years to analyse the results – a faster method was urgently needed. Hollerith had an idea based on the old Jacquard loom. He produced cards and punched holes in different positions to indicate information needed in the census. For example, a hole could be punched in the first 'box' for a man, the second box for a woman, and so on. Now, to interpret the results, he passed the punched cards over a tray of mercury above which were vertical metal pins connected to an electric circuit. Whenever a hole appeared, one of the pins dropped through the hole and touched the mercury. Because mercury conducts electricity this acted as a switch and completed the electrical circuit. In this way all the holes could be counted by the machine in a fraction of the time taken by manual calculation. The 1890 census was analysed in one third of the previous time, and

The computer

1 The Jacquard loom

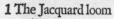

2 Charles Babbage and his 'analytical engine'

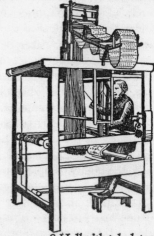

3 Hollerith tabulator, used in the U.S. census, 1890

4 Ferranti Mark 1 computer at Manchester University, 1948

5 A modern word-processor

Hollerith punched-card systems became widely used in many parts of the world. The company formed by Hollerith later became part of International Business Machines (IBM).

In 1939 Howard H. Aiken of Harvard University in the United States, together with a group of engineers from IBM, started work on an electrical digital computer, based on existing machines but fully automatic. It took until 1944 before the Automatic Sequence Controlled Calculator, or Harvard Mark I, was completed and operating. It was a large machine, over 15 metres (50 feet) long and 2.4 metres (8 feet) high – and very noisy. Information was fed in on punched cards but the machine was controlled by punched paper tape – as were the later electronic computers, which were already being developed.

The first electronic computer was invented in 1946 by J. Presper Eckert and John W. Mauchly of the University of Pennsylvania. It was called the Electronic Numerical Integrator and Calculator (ENIAC), and it operated more than 1000 times faster than the electric machines.

The new computer was a large machine weighing 30,500 kilogrammes (30 tons), and containing some 18,000 radio valves which generated an enormous amount of heat – and frequently failed. In fact the whole project very nearly failed in its early stages when Mauchly's original design report was lost. Luckily his secretary still had the shorthand notes and the report was salvaged.

With Eckert's help the design was developed into a working computer and the two inventors set up a company. This was sold to Remington Rand in 1951, and in the same year the first commercially-manufactured electronic computers were produced: Remington Rand supplied their Univac I to the U.S. Census Bureau and in Britain the first Ferranti Mark I machine was installed at Manchester University.

24 *Radar and Microwave Ovens*

At first sight it may seem rather odd to link radar with microwave ovens, yet they are closely related because one evolved from the other. Many books claim that radar was invented by the Scottish scientist Robert Alexander Watson-Watt, but this is an over-simplification of a very complicated story which, at the time, was shrouded in mystery. During the 1930s many nations were investigating the possibilities of beaming radio signals on to distant objects and measuring the echo. These signals could then be used to determine the direction of the object and its distance from the station. The idea had been known for some time, indeed during the 1880s Heinrich Hertz, who contributed towards the invention of radio with his spark experiment, noticed that the radio signals generated by his sparks were reflected from the pillars of his laboratory. Many other scientists studied radio waves and their reflections over the next fifty years.

By 1933 a German scientist called Rudolph Kühnold was developing a practical system, and early in the following year it was ready for testing. In Kiel harbour he transmitted a signal and received an echo from the battleship *Hesse* anchored 550 metres (600 yards) away. Later in the year Kühnold picked up a ship 11 kilometres (7 miles) away, and he even detected an aircraft in his beam – but this was a lucky accident! After these successful tests the German authorities provided money for his work to continue.

By 1934 the British government were taking an interest in radio waves, but their interest was to produce a 'death ray' which would paralyse aircraft in flight. Robert Watson-Watt and his assistant A. F. Wilkins were given the task of investigating the death ray: they soon showed that it was not feasible. Instead Watson-Watt produced a report entitled *Detection and Location of Aircraft by Radio Methods*. On 26th February, 1935, he gave a practical demonstration, locating a bomber flying at 1800 metres (6000 feet) when it was still 13 kilometres (8 miles) away. His equipment was very simple: a short-wave radio signal was transmitted by the BBC Station at Daventry and the echo was displayed on a cathode-ray tube housed, with the rest of the equipment, in the back of a Morris van.

From this promising start Watson-Watt improved the range and accuracy of his equipment, and by spring 1939 Britain had a chain of twenty *radiolocation* stations around the coast from the Isle of Wight to the Firth of Forth. By this time Germany had about eight stations and both countries were desperately trying to keep the stations with their large aerials secret. Other countries were also engaged in experiments, including France, Japan and the United States. The first American demonstration took place in June 1936 and in about 1940 Commander S. M. Tucker of the U.S. Navy invented the word *radar*. It was a code word for RAdio Detection And Ranging: Britain officially adopted the name radar in 1943.

During the Second World War British radar played a vital part by warning the RAF fighter squadrons whenever enemy bombers approached the coastline. But Britain was well ahead of other countries in another form of radar – a system which was small enough to be carried by aircraft. The secret of this airborne radar was a small device called a *cavity magnetron* which could transmit radio pulses equivalent to those produced by a large broadcasting transmitter. The cavity magnetron was invented during 1940 by two scientists at Birmingham University, John Turton Randall and H. A. H. Boot. British night-fighter pilots aided by

Radar and microwave ovens

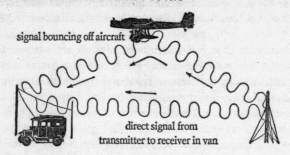

signal bouncing off aircraft

direct signal from
transmitter to receiver in van

The Daventry experiment, 1935

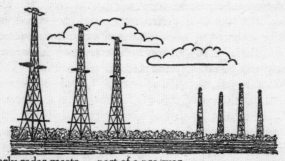

Early radar masts — part of a pre-war
chain along the east coast of Britain

The original magnetron —
now at the Science Museum, London

Microwave
oven

Airborne Interception radar were extremely successful, and to hide the real reason for this success the story was put about that they ate raw carrots which helped them to see in the dark!

As so often happens, wartime inventions are adapted for peacetime use, and radar was no exception. Aircraft and ships rely heavily on radar to control movements and avoid collisions, but the cavity magnetron was adapted for a very different role – it became part of a microwave oven. Food in a microwave oven is bombarded with short-wave electromagnetic radiation from a cavity magnetron: these waves are shorter than normal radio waves but longer than infrared, which can also be used for cooking. The food absorbs energy from the microwaves and in minutes, or even seconds, it is cooked. The first microwave cooker was produced by a company in the United States called Raytheon Inc. and the new cooker soon became very popular, particularly with owners of restaurants and snack-bars.

Most non-stick saucepans are coated with a plastic material called polytetrafluoroethylene or 'PTFE' and their invention is a strange story spread over many years. In 1938 a scientist working for the large du Pont company accidentally discovered PTFE while experimenting with the gas tetrafluoroethylene. Dr Roy J. Plunket was going to use the gas in the freezing unit of a refrigerator, and having made up a supply he stored it in a cylinder. When Plunket opened the cylinder several weeks later he discovered that some of the gas had changed into a new plastic – it had *polymerised* into polytetrafluoroethylene. The new material had some interesting properties: it was very slippery and it resisted many highly corrosive materials. In 1944 PTFE was placed on the secret list, and employed to make containers for some of the corrosive materials which were being used in the United States nuclear research programme.

After the Second World War, PTFE's unusual properties were adapted for many and varied jobs. It was produced under a variety of trade names: in the United States du Pont called it *Teflon*; in Britain ICI used the name *Fluon*. It was used to protect containers, pipes, valves and pumps against corrosive liquids and gases. It could stand up to an enormous range of temperatures from very cold to very hot, and it was an extremely good electrical insulator. Its slippery surface was used by machine designers, who discovered that bearings coated with PTFE would run for years without oiling, and saw that blades coated with PTFE would cut metal with much less effort.

The idea of adapting PTFE's slippery surface for cooking utensils occurred independently to several people in the 1950s, but for domestic use credit is usually given to a

Non-stick pans

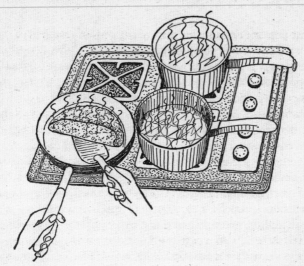

French engineer, Mark Grégoire. Fishing was one of Grégoire's hobbies and being an engineer he knew about the slippery properties of PTFE – so he used these properties to prevent his fishing line from sticking. When his wife heard about this she asked if anything could be done to stop food sticking to her pans. Mark Grégoire found that a coating of PTFE did the trick, indeed it was so successful that in 1955 he founded a company called Tefal and non-stick saucepans went into production. During 1956 non-stick saucepans were pioneered in Britain by Philip Harben, the television chef who founded the Harbenware brand. These non-stick pans of the later 1950s were relatively expensive and it was not until 1962 that the du Pont Company went into large-scale production in the United States. The domestic non-stick saucepan had arrived by way of a refrigerator gas, nuclear research, engineering bearings and a fishing rod.

26 Hovercraft

The hovercraft can travel over land or water supported on a cushion of air. It 'flies' at just a few feet above the ground and is remarkably manoeuvrable as it can travel forwards, backwards or sideways. Many pilots of conventional aircraft discovered this cushion of air as they were about to land – it would cause them to float along the runway much to their dismay. In 1955 a British inventor called Christopher Cockerell patented an idea to make use of this cushion of air, and so the hovercraft was born. Other names are sometimes used to describe this new form of transport including air cushion vehicles, ground-effect machines, surface-effect ships or surface-effect vessels. The success of the hovercraft compared with that of any other new form of transport was phenomenal. In just four years it emerged from the experimental stage to become a practical vehicle. Even the aeroplane took almost twenty years.

Christopher Cockerell was an electronics engineer who was interested in boats as a hobby. He studied them scientifically, and was especially interested in the problem of water-resistance to high-speed boats. He decided that the answer was to separate the 'boat' from the water by a cushion of air. Cockerell had observed that skates and sledge-runners travel freely over ice, using a thin layer of water as a cushion. To produce a cushion of air he decided to fit a large fan, which would blow air into the space beneath his punt. He also experimented with a high-speed launch, but he had a major problem as the air escaped around the edges of both vessels. He considered using rigid walls or curtains extending down to the surface of the water. However, rigid walls would not be very effective over waves, as the air might escape.

Cockerell next investigated a flexible curtain of water: this proved to be heavy and not very practical. Then he carried out a very simple, do-it-yourself experiment which proved to be the key to success for his invention. An empty Lyons coffee tin was placed upside-down over a smaller tin, also upside down. Air from a modified vacuum cleaner was blown into the large tin through a hole in its inverted base. This air emerged downwards from the 'annular' space between the two tins, and on to the pan of some kitchen scales. Cockerell discovered that if he measured the force of the air on the pan first without the tins, then with the tins, the increase was amazing – he was producing three times the force. Now he had solved his problem, for he could use a 'curtain' of high-pressure air ejected all round the edge of the craft. This continuous flow of air was angled downwards and inwards so that it provided not only a curtain, but also a supply of air for the cushion.

Cockerell tried out his idea on a model which worked very well, and he took it to London for a demonstration over the carpets of government offices in Whitehall. The officials were impressed with the new invention and put it on the Secret List, but they did not take the matter any further.

Like most inventors, Cockerell did not give in easily to technical or political problems and his persistence eventually paid off – a full-size hovercraft was ordered from a company called Saunders-Roe Ltd of Cowes on the Isle of Wight (now part of British Hovercraft Corporation). The SR.NI appeared early in 1959. It was almost circular in shape, about 9 metres (30 feet) in diameter and weighed 4000 kilogrammes (about 4 tons). A distinguishing feature was the large, white air-intake, looking like an enormous funnel, situated in the centre of the flat, circular hull. Inside this intake, or duct, was a 213-cm (7-ft) ducted fan driven by an Alvis 'Leonides' piston engine of 435 h.p. Two-thirds of the air from this fan supplied a double air-curtain angled

125

The hovercraft

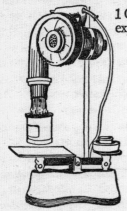

1 Cockerell's original air-cushion experiment

2 Cockerell filming his first hovercraft model

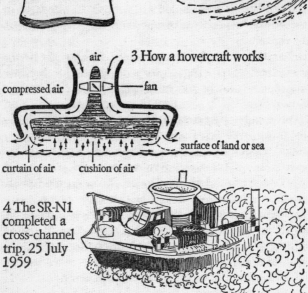

3 How a hovercraft works

air

compressed air — fan

surface of land or sea

curtain of air cushion of air

4 The SR-N1 completed a cross-channel trip, 25 July 1959

inwards, while the remainder was ejected as jets to provide propulsion.

In this form the SR.N1 could 'fly' at a height of 230mm (9 inches) and travel at almost 50 km/h (31 mph). It made its first free 'hover' on 30th May, 1959, at Cowes, and on 25th July the new hovercraft made history when it crossed the English Channel from Calais to Dover on the fiftieth anniversary of Blériot's first cross-Channel flight in 1909. As experience was gained, improvements were made to the SR.N1. Flexible skirts were fitted to improve the sealing around the air-cushion, and small jet engines were installed which increased its speed to 120 km/h (75 mph).

Hovercraft soon became very popular because they were so much faster than conventional ships which had to force their way through the water instead of skimming above it. Hovercraft can also travel across ice, sandbanks, shallows and rapids, deserts and marshland. Normally they do not need any road or track, but a special 'hovertrain' has been invented which rides on a very thin cushion of air between the vehicle and a reinforced-concrete track. (See Great Invention number 30, page 138.)

The use of the hovercraft's air-cushion principle does not stop at transport. It has already extended into the home and garden where air-cushion vacuum cleaners and lawn-mowers can reduce the effort of pulling and pushing. In factories, the air-cushion can replace the conveyor-belt as a means of transporting heavy loads easily. In hospitals, a soothing cushion may be used to support a badly burned or injured patient. It is a far cry from Christopher Cockerell's punt to a hospital bed, but the air-cushion still has not finished extending its sphere of influence.

27 Lasers

The word 'laser' has become part of our language, but really it is an abbreviation for Light Amplification by Stimulated Emission of Radiation. A laser is a very concentrated beam of light with all the light waves in step: this beam can be so intense that it will cut the hardest materials such as a diamond.

The story of the laser starts with Albert Einstein, who in 1917 said that it should be possible to stimulate an atom and make it release energy in the form of light. This idea was not demonstrated by practical experiments until 1960, when an American physicist, Theodore H. Maiman, constructed the first successful laser at Malibu, California. Maiman pumped energy into a ruby crystal and made it emit a powerful flash of red light. From this followed a whole range of lasers, producing continuous beams of light from one end of the spectrum to the other. The heart of the laser is the crystal, gas or liquid into which energy is pumped, for this dictates the type of laser beam emitted. Beams range from a low-powered helium-neon red laser to a powerful 'death ray'.

Lasers, and uses to which they can be put, are still being invented and it is difficult to predict the future of these inventions. Lasers can be used to measure distances: for example, a very accurate measurement of the moon's distance from the earth was taken by aiming a beam at the moon and reflecting it back to earth from a special mirror placed on the moon by Apollo astronauts. Weather forecasters can use lasers to follow movements of air in the atmosphere. Medical uses of lasers are expanding year by year as research workers develop new techniques for eye

Lasers

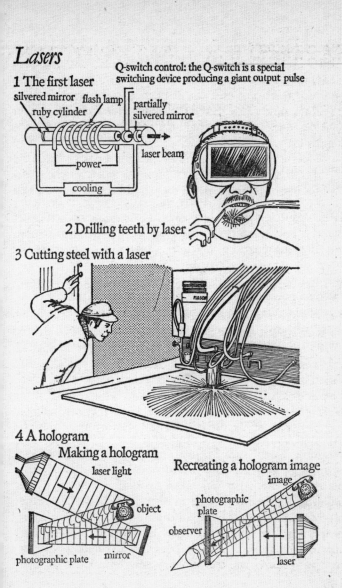

1 The first laser

Q-switch control: the Q-switch is a special switching device producing a giant output pulse

silvered mirror flash lamp partially silvered mirror

ruby cylinder

laser beam

power

cooling

2 Drilling teeth by laser

3 Cutting steel with a laser

4 A hologram

Making a hologram

laser light

object

photographic plate mirror

Recreating a hologram image

image

photographic plate

observer

laser

operations, tooth 'drilling' and even cancer treatment: lasers can be carried into the body by a fibre-optic tube (see page 133) and remove growths without the need for surgery. Industrial lasers are used to cut diamonds and steel, and for welding operations. Lasers have the great advantage that they do not heat the surrounding area, which can be a problem with conventional flame-cutters and welding equipment.

Perhaps the most promising future for the laser lies in the field of communications, for a laser resembles a radio transmitter but has a great advantage – it can carry many million radio transmissions on a single laser beam. The disadvantage is that, like all light, a laser does not penetrate fog or cloud very well; a solution to this problem is still being sought. In outer space, where there are no clouds, lasers may well be the means of communication for the future.

Another exciting possibility is three-dimensional television based on the *hologram.* Holography is related to photography since it records an object or scene on film; but in holography a laser is used instead of normal light. A three-dimensional image or hologram can be re-created by a laser and this *hologram image* can be looked at from different angles, unlike the familiar stereo-picture produced by photography, which presents just one view in depth.

Finally and further in the future, lasers may revolutionise nuclear energy. At present nuclear reactors make use of a reaction corresponding to the atomic bomb, but the more powerful hydrogen bomb reaction might be harnessed with the help of lasers.

Perhaps the most attractive – but least useful – example of fibre optics is the popular decorative lamp which looks like a horse's tail with coloured lights coming from the ends of the 'hairs'. These hairs are in fact thin fibres of glass, and light is shone into them at their base, where they are held in a tight bundle. The source of light may contain a rotating wheel carrying different coloured filters so the light changes colour. Light travelling along a fibre gives rise to the name 'fibre optics'.

A predecessor of fibre optics is the periscope which enables us to see around corners or over objects which obstruct our view – such as people's heads in a crowd watching a parade. Light from one of the floats in the parade travels over the heads of the people and into the top of the periscope, where it is bent downwards by a mirror or a prism. At the bottom of the periscope the light is bent horizontally into our eyes and we can see the float. While travelling from the object to our eyes the light has been bent twice, but in between these points it travels in straight lines. To make light travel along a curved path was a challenge to many scientists and inventors over the years.

There was a major problem whenever attempts were made to carry light along a curved rod or fibre: at the first bend, the light travelled straight on and escaped from the rod. In 1926 John Logie Baird, one of the inventors of television, suggested the idea of keeping light inside a tube or rod by using a reflective surface to prevent it escaping, but he did not have any practical success. A solution was not found until the 1950s: in the Netherlands A. C. S. van Heel, and in London, H. H. Hopkins and N. S. Kapany developed

Fibre optics

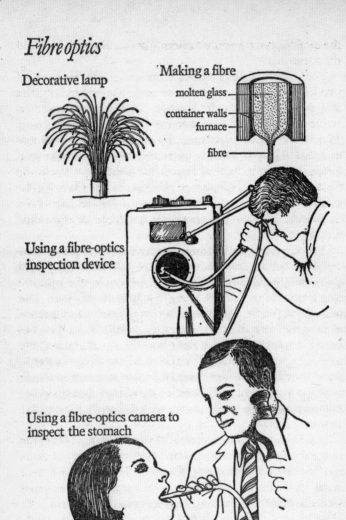

Decorative lamp

Making a fibre

molten glass
container walls
furnace
fibre

Using a fibre-optics inspection device

Using a fibre-optics camera to inspect the stomach

the modern system of fibre optics – in fact Kapany first used the name in 1956.

The secret of fibre optics is to make the fibre out of two kinds of glass, an inner core made in one kind of glass and an outer coating in another. This outer coating acts rather like a mirror and prevents the light from escaping. The two kinds of glass must be carefully selected so that each has the most suitable 'refractive index' to ensure total internal reflection, which means the light stays inside the fibre despite any curvature or movement. The fibres can be made very fine indeed – far finer than a human hair – and then used in bundles containing hundreds of individual fibres.

A flexible bundle of fibres can be used to examine inaccessible parts of a machine: some of the fibres carry light down to illuminate the interior part, while the operator looks down other fibres to see the illuminated part. This same principle can be used on the human body: for instance, a bronchoscope allows a doctor to look down a patient's throat and examine parts right out of normal sight. Other internal parts of the body can be examined by specially designed probes using fibre optics and many of these can also be used to take photographs. Some of the fibre probes are so fine that they can be inserted into the body through a hypodermic syringe.

In addition to carrying normal light, the optical fibres can also carry lasers and this may open up whole new industries in the future. For example, a single fibre carrying a laser beam can carry many thousand telephone conversations with less interference than the present electrical system.

The transistor is one example of a 'semiconductor', another is the 'cat's whisker' used in the earliest radio sets.

A cat's whisker actually consisted of a fine wire just touching the surface of a crystal made from a semi-conducting material such as silicon or galena. The cat's whisker or 'crystal detector' allowed an electric current to flow in one direction but not the other, and it formed a vital part of radio receivers during the 1920s. It was superseded by improved radio valves, but when the transistor was invented in 1948 the radio valve was itself superseded.

The inventors responsible for the transistor worked at the Bell Telephone Laboratories in the United States. William Shockley led a research team which, during the Second World War, worked on a silicon detector of microwaves in radar. After the War, Shockley, ably assisted by John Bardeen and Walter H. Brattain, produced the transistor. This was soon able to do virtually all the things a radio valve could do, but the transistor was more reliable, stronger, smaller, cheaper and it used much less electrical power. Further, when switched on a transistor radio would function immediately; valves needed time to warm up. For their contribution to science, the three inventors of the transistor were awarded the 1956 Nobel Prize for physics.

Another innovation occurred at about the same time: this was called a *printed circuit* and it replaced the old method of joining together the many components of a radio, or other electronic equipment, with wires and soldered joints (which were liable to give trouble). A board of insulating material was coated with a thin layer of copper, which is an excellent conductor of electricity, and then a complete circuit was drawn out and printed on the copper by a photographic process. This resulted in all the 'wires' and some of the components being marked out by a protective film. The board was then immersed in an acid bath which dissolved away all the uncovered copper, leaving just the required circuit – in copper. Additions could easily be soldered to the basic circuit, but the number of joints was reduced to a minimum to increase reliability and reduce costs. The printed circuit and the transistor rejuvenated the radio industry: the new 'miniaturised' radios were much cheaper and more reliable than the old fashioned versions fitted with valves. In a few years millions of people all over the world either owned or shared a 'tranny'!

During the 1960s the electronics industry was still moving rapidly ahead, stimulated by the United States space research projects, which required even smaller components. Microminiaturised, integrated circuits on silicon 'chips' were the key to the new electronics revolution. *Microminiaturised components* are so small that it is difficult to understand how they can possibly work; for instance a circuit containing 10,000 components can be reduced to just a few millimetres in diameter. The 10,000 components make up an *integrated circuit* in which all the transistors, resistors and other components are built into the circuit and not attached afterwards. So the printed circuit was a stepping stone to the integrated circuit but there was a further step and a very vital one. The integrated circuit is designed on a large-scale drawing and then photographed. By a complex photographic process it is reduced in size and etched on to a slice of a silicon crystal. The reduction in size is so great that a 5-cm circle of silicon may contain several hundred complete circuits. Each of these circuits is known as a *chip* and a typical chip would be about 1–2mm square and 0.25mm thick.

Transistors, and silicon chips

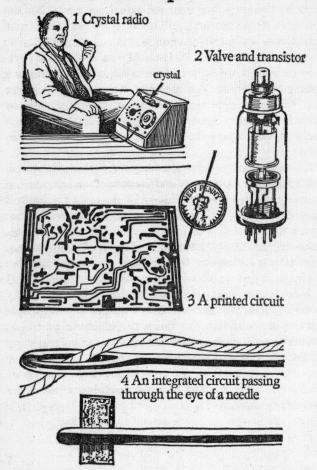

1 Crystal radio

crystal

2 Valve and transistor

NEW PENNY

3 A printed circuit

4 An integrated circuit passing through the eye of a needle

With an invention as complex as the integrated circuit on a micro-chip, much of the work had to be done by teams of research workers rather than individual inventors. But the man who started the ball rolling was Jack Kilby of Texas Instruments who patented the first integrated circuit in the United States during 1959. He used a material called germanium instead of silicon and his circuit would have been a nightmare to produce in any numbers. An improved design using silicon was being developed at the same time by another inventor, Robert Noyce of the rival Fairchild company, and as so often happens there were patent disputes.

The micro-chip has already revolutionised radios, watches, pocket calculators and computers and its use has spread to car ignition systems, washing machine controls and television games. These are just a few examples: the list is long and ever increasing. New developments include information services presented on existing television sets, home links to a computer by telephone, and word processors which speed up a typist's work and newspaper production. If these new machines cut down the number of workers doing a particular job, then the invention will lead to some people being made redundant. But this is not a new problem – it happened when Hargreaves invented the spinning jenny and Meikle invented the threshing machine. Perhaps the lesson to be learnt from the past would be to slow down the rate of change in order to allow people to adjust to the new inventions.

30 *The Linear Electric Motor and Magnetic Levitation*

The first invention described in this collection of great inventions was the wheel – a simple thing which has withstood the test of time. The final pair of inventions linked together could make the wheel redundant on railways of the future. A linear electric motor to move the train along its track and a magnetic levitation system to support it have already been invented, but whether they will work in practice and withstand the test of time remains to be seen.

Most of the railways throughout the world use a track consisting of two steel rails on which wheels roll. Now, however, there are two new tracks available and neither requires wheels. A variation of the hovercraft has already been mentioned (invention number 26; page 127). This train riding on a thin cushion of air between the vehicle and a concrete track has become known as a *tracked hovercraft*. The second track without wheels uses magnetism to support the train. A simple experiment with two magnets will easily show that two north poles repel each other. Now if the magnets are held one above the other, the lower one represents a series of fixed magnets in the track, while the upper one represents the train. Instead of using permanent magnets, the full-size system has electromagnets (magnets produced by passing an electric current through a coil of wire wrapped around a core of soft iron). By controlling the current passing through the coils, the height of the train above its track can be controlled. This is called *magnetic levitation*.

Both the tracked hovercraft and the magnetic levitation system have the great advantage of very low resistance to movement because they do not have to overcome the friction inherent with wheels and their bearings. On the other hand they cannot be powered in the usual way, through driving wheels. They can have an external propeller or jet engine as used to power aircraft or they could be propelled by the new linear electric motor.

Most conventional electric motors consist of a cylindrical outer casing with a series of electro-magnetic coils mounted on its inside surface – this is called the 'stator'. Inside the stator there is a rotating steel cylinder or 'rotor' in which are set a number of copper or aluminium bars. Current is supplied to the stator coils with the result that the rotor rotates and the motor is working. Now to convert the idea of a rotary motor to a linear motor, cut the stator at the top and let each side unwind until it is lying along a horizontal line. Change the rotor from a cylinder to a flat plate of aluminium and switch on the current to the stator coils. The plate will move off to the left or right and this is the principle of a linear electric motor. A train would require an extended stator built into the track and the equivalent of the aluminium plate built into the moving vehicle, or the positions could be reversed, with the plate built into the track and the stator coils carried in the train.

The idea of a linear electric motor is far from new, for it was invented in 1845 by Sir Charles Wheatstone, of King's College, London. Wheatstone built a linear motor for demonstration purposes but very little happened for the next hundred years. During the Second World War a linear electric motor was built into a catapult for launching aircraft from the deck of a ship. A steam-powered catapult was also developed and this proved to be more successful so the 'electropult' was abandoned, although a similar device has been used to test cars under crash conditions by hurling them into a wall.

During the early 1960s inventors in several countries

The linear electric motor, and magnetic levitation

A linear motor in diagrammatic form

conventional motor

linear motor

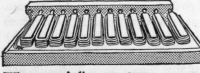

Wheatstone's linear motor

Laithwaite's model train

Hovertrain, 1971

Japanese HSST, 1976, using
magnetic levitation

were working on plans for high-speed trains powered by linear electric motors. One of the foremost inventors was Professor Eric Laithwaite of Imperial College, London. In 1947 Laithwaite began working on the problem – at the time he was not designing linear motors for trains but for high-speed shuttles in looms. Laithwaite's high-speed shuttles powered by linear motors were a success and he then turned his attention to high-speed trains.

In 1967 the British government set up a company called Tracked Hovercraft Ltd, to develop a high-speed hovertrain. Professor Laithwaite helped to design the linear motor which used a continuous fixed plate laid flat in the track and electrical coils inside the train. This arrangement required an electrical supply to the moving train in order to power the coils and the blowers which provided the air cushion. Current was supplied through a sliding contact on a separate rail – similar to the idea used by British Rail's Southern Region.

A short track was built near Cambridge and a test vehicle was successfully demonstrated in 1971. At the time this British hovertrain was more promising than its French, American, German or Japanese rivals but it has not led to a hovertrain carrying passengers in Britain. The high cost of a new track when conventional railway lines exist really rules out the hovertrain – but it is a different story when a completely new railway system is being planned. For instance in Japan a high-speed rail link was needed between Tokyo's new international airport and the city centre. In 1976 a prototype High Speed Surface Transport (HSST) car was demonstrated for the first time: it was powered by a linear motor and supported by magnetic levitation. By 1978 a speed of 308 km/h (191 mph) had been reached, which was slightly higher than the operating speed of the full-size train, designed to carry 120 passengers. In Germany too, a number of linear motor plus magnetic levitation research vehicles have been built and tested in recent years. They are proposed for links between a city centre and its airport or suburban areas.

Here is an invention in the balance – it may eliminate the wheel from railways of the future or it could fade into obscurity.

Index

More Beaver Books

We hope you have enjoyed this Beaver Book. Here are some of the other titles:

Famous Lives: Scientists and Inventors A Beaver original. Want to know who invented the saxophone, or who discovered the electron? Read all about the amazing achievements of 180 great scientists and inventors from ancient times right down to today. Devised by James Moore, written by Norman Dahl and illustrated by Peter Dennis

Why does a Glow-worm Glow? A Beaver original. Dozens of answers to intriguing questions on science topics, illustrated throughout by Mike Jackson and with a lively text by Professor Eric Laithwaite, well known as a contributor to the BBC radio programme *Dial-a-Scientist*

The Beaver Book of the Air A Beaver original. The thrilling story of man's conquest of the air, from the basic principles of flight to supersonic jets. Written by J. D. Storer and illustrated by John Batchelor and Peter Dennis

The Beaver Book of the Sea A Beaver original. The story of the sea, with a look at its tides, currents and winds, flora and fauna, the history of shipbuilding and the sailor's life, written by John Davies and illustrated by Albany Wiseman

These and many other Beavers are available from your local bookshop or newsagent, or can be ordered direct from: Hamlyn Paperback Cash Sales, PO Box 11, Falmouth, Cornwall TR10 9EN. Send a cheque or postal order, made payable to The Hamlyn Publishing Group, for the price of the book plus postage at the following rates:
UK: 30p for the first book, 15p for the second book, and 12p for each additional book ordered to a maximum charge of £1.29;
BFPO and EIRE: 30p for the first book, 15p for the second book plus 12p per copy for the next 7 books, thereafter 6p per book;
OVERSEAS: 50p for the first book and 15p for each extra book.

New Beavers are published every month and if you would like the *Beaver Bulletin*, which gives a complete list of books and prices, including new titles, send a large stamped addressed envelope to:

Beaver Bulletin
Hamlyn Paperbacks
Banda House
Cambridge Grove
Hammersmith
London W6 0LE

349233